C000284925

fresh and healthy

teas

fresh and healthy

teas

Delicious teas and infusions for health and vitality

Tammy Safi

London · New York · Sydney · Toronto

A CBS COMPANY

Contents

Recipes

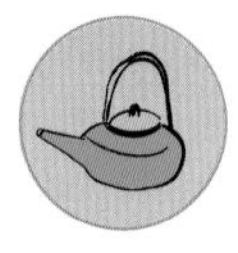

INTRODUCTION

My love for tea started years ago. When I was a child, my father would brew a strong, milky, sweet tea for both of us. As he was pouring it, he would ask, "One or two teaspoons, Tammy?" My answer was always two, but he asked, nevertheless. The time we spent sipping a cup of tea was our time. We still sit and drink tea together, but today the tea is more likely to be lemon grass or cinnamon. My father continues to ask, "Any sugar, Tammy?" Even though I always reply, "No thanks, Dad. No sugar," he asks every time.

Now a qualified herbalist and nutritionist, my interest in the therapeutic properties of plants and herbs also started many years ago, when I lived in Lebanon. My newborn baby suffered from colic, and one morning my nosy neighbor heard him screaming. She barged her way into my kitchen—as she always didwith a handful of sweet-smelling seeds. I watched her infuse the seeds and witnessed my first cup of herb tea: aniseed. The tea worked like magic. My son was soon out of his misery and fast asleep.

In this book I explore tea as we know it today: its origins, where it is grown and cultivated, and how it has been used for thousands of years for both pleasure and medicinal purposes, particularly green tea. The recipes that follow include those that can be used for health and wellbeing, and those that are commonly drunk in Asia, along with some interesting floral and fruit blends.

Tea was my constant companion during the writing of this book, and nothing gives me more pleasure than passing on my knowledge of this delectable brew. Most of the ingredients in this book are readily available at supermarkets, natural foods stores, or Asian, Indian, and Lebanese grocery stores, or Chinese herb stores. However, it is well worth growing your own herbs. There is nothing like the fragrance of freshly cut lavender or yarrow. If you plant just a few different herbs each month, you will have a herb garden with the most tantalizing aromas before you know it.

Asian Teas: A Way of Life

Asians have a great deal of respect for tea. They serve it with every meal to help facilitate digestion. It is also served to guests as a warm welcoming beverage. The tea plant, *Camellia sinensis,* is a beautiful evergreen native to Southeast Asia. It is grown mostly in China, India, Indonesia, Sri Lanka and Japan. It grows best in the mountains, far above sea level, where the days are sunny, the nights rainy and the air clean and fresh. The best green teas are grown at 5000 feet (1525 meters) above sea level.

It's All in the Process

Plantation pickers rise before sunrise and spend the day expertly picking the precious leaves with just a swift flick of their fingers. When a basket is full, it is returned to the factory; the leaves then undergo a number of delicate and important stages before the tea is ready to brew. These processes include:

Fermentation: The leaves are kept in a moist 72°–82°F (30°C) atmosphere so that they warm up and then begin to cool. If the temperature is any higher, the tea will be tainted with a burnt taste. Any lower, and the fermentation process will stop. Fermentation ends just before the leaves begin to cool. This can take one to three hours. The leaves are then dried in machines at 175°F (80°C) for twenty minutes. If the tea is fired for too long, the leaves will lose their flavor. On the other hand, if they are not fired long enough, mold will form.

Withering: Tea leaves are spread over screens or woven straw mats, which are then stacked on top of each other so that warm air can circulate around the leaves, ensuring that mold doesn't form. They are left to dry for 24 hours, after which the leaves are crisp and completely dry.

Pan-firing: This method is usually reserved for the production of green tea. The leaves are constantly stirred in woks over a consistent heat until they are dry.

Steaming: This method is usually used in Japan for green-tea production. The tea leaves are steamed in trays over boiling water to soften them and prevent oxidation.

Rolling: This can be done by hand or machine, and it is a method usually reserved for green tea. The tea leaves are rolled into curls, twists, and other shapes, which affect the flavor during infusion.

Naming Teas

Teas of the world are classified in a number of ways. One is by the size and shape of the processed leaf. Another is by the way it is processed. Tea leaves are grouped by hand. Traditional manufacturing yields a large leaf with smaller broken pieces, or grades. The leaves are spread over mats according to whether they are whole or broken, as well as according to their size. The leaves are named according to their length: "dust" is less than 0.04 inch (1 mm) in length, and "fanning" is less than 0.06 inch (1.5 mm).

Another way of classifying a tea is by the country or district where it is grown, such as China, India, Ceylon, or Japan.

Different teas work best at different times, depending on what you are doing and your state of health. In Asia, each tea is drunk for its own specific effect and taste. Black tea has a significant amount of caffeine, is warming, and acts as a digestive, while green tea is cooling and cleansing, with low amounts of caffeine. Black tea is often drunk in the morning or when you need a boost, but because green tea helps to reduce cholesterol by lowering blood lipids, it is best drunk with meals or with a sweet between meals.

The History of Asian Teas

Tea is made by steeping or boiling chopped plant material—roots, leaves, and flowers—for a specified amount of time. It is a warm, soothing drink that brings to mind good company, good times and happy days. The art of making the humble cup of tea has been lovingly passed down through the generations for thousands of centuries.

Chinese Origins

Tea is believed to have originated in China in 2737BC. Legend has it that Emperor Sh'eng Nung was spending a day in the countryside. He was sipping a cup of hot water, as was his custom, when a few leaves from a tree blew into the cup. The aroma from the mix was so enticing that he sipped the brew and a new beverage was born. Since then, there has been a lot of experimenting with boiling water and the leaf of that evergreen, *Camellia sinensis*.

During the Sung Dynasty, 960–1279AD, tea making was considered an art form. As tea was rare and costly, affordable only by the elite, competitions would take place among royal families to determine who could perfect the most skillful techniques for making tea. These competitions made tea a highly desired beverage. Before long, its use spread and green tea became the most popular of all.

Many provinces created distinctive methods of brewing. The Fujian province, for example, rolled tea leaves into a ball. Pieces were scraped off these balls and then placed in a glazed bowl. Hot water was added and the mixture was stirred until a white froth formed. The longer the froth lasted, the better. The liquid tea, however, had to be clear.

Picked in India

Tea is believed to have been introduced into India around 500AD by Siddhartha, the prince who became the Buddha. It is said that Siddhartha left India, pledging to remain awake for nine years in order to meditate and travel for enlightenment. After five years, he was overcome by sleep. While resting beside a green bush, he picked some of its leaves and chewed them. They revived him, giving him alertness and energy. Siddhartha continued his journey with this newfound tea. When he returned to India he brought tea seeds to be planted.

India became the largest tea-growing country when Robert Fortune, a botanist and spy for the East India Company, transported 23,000 young plants and 17,000 seedlings from China to India between 1848 and 1851. Fortune wrote many best-selling books, full of adventure and excitement, about his travels from China to India. The Indians adopted the English practice of serving tea with milk and sugar. They also had their own "local" tea, masala chai, which is a fragrant, sweet, warming tea, made with milk and spices.

Revered in Japan

Dengyo Daishi, a Buddhist monk, is generally credited with bringing tea to Japan after traveling to China around 803–805AD. He did so after he noticed that tea had the ability to keep the monks in China awake and alert during long hours of meditation and prayer.

The first Japanese book about tea is called *The Book Of Tea Sanitation*, by Eisai, a Buddhist monk, and was published in 1211AD. It is also known as *Maintaining Health By Drinking Tea*. In his book, Eisai describes the benefits of drinking tea and how it could be used to treat some illnesses. After this, Japanese monks took tea drinking to a different level, embracing it within their spiritual ceremonies and beliefs.

Tea is thought to have reached the rest of Asia by the end of the sixth century, thanks to Zen Buddhist monks, who traveled widely.

Migrating West

The earliest reference to tea in Europe is in 1559. A Venetian citizen wrote a book called *Voyages and Travels*, which mentions chai catai (tea of China). R.L. Wickham, of the English East India Company, is thought to have been the first to mention tea in England in 1615. Before tea came along, the English drank more coffee than any other nation.

The much-loved Assam tea is believed to have been discovered by Major Robert Bruce, a Scotsman, who found tea bushes growing on both sides of the Brahmaputra River in Assam in 1823. Plantations were soon set up, areas cleared, and the first tea from Assam was auctioned in England in 1839. Assam tea lovers believe that this tea has the strength to cure all weaknesses.

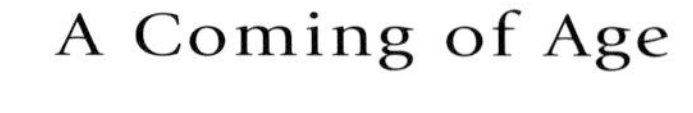

A Coming of Age

These days, there are hundreds of different grades, qualities, and varieties of tea. Dedicated tea drinkers take tea as seriously as cheese tasters do cheese, or wine connoisseurs wine. And tea has moved beyond the black tea that we first think of to include many other plant ingredients.

Herbs may be more familiar to people as a culinary flavoring. Rosemary, thyme, mint, and sage are common in Western cuisine. But herbs, as well many other plants, including fruits, can be made into teas using either one herb or a mixture of several. You can also add flowers and spices.

Herbal teas are becoming more popular because of their strong medicinal properties. Hippocrates' wise words, "Let your food be your medicine and your medicine be your food," are often quoted for their truth and efficacy, and they are certainly appropriate as far as herbal teas are concerned.

Floral and fruit teas have the added advantage of bringing scent and beauty to a cup of tea. The variety of dried fruits and flowers available, mixed and matched in different combinations, can create a fragrant and attractive beverage to delight family and friends.

If you have a cold, infection, or a feeling of dampness in your body, it is best to drink diaphoretic teas such as ginger and sage. These teas encourage sweating and should be drunk warm or hot until you break out in a sweat. Bitter-tasting teas, such as dandelion, chamomile, and green or jasmine, can enhance digestion and decrease allergic reactions, and they should be drunk before meals. The bitter taste stimulates the flow of digestive juices, preventing bloating and discomfort.

Tea and Your Health

Since ancient times, humans have experimented with nearly every plant and discovered which are safe and which are poisonous. However, it takes a trained herbalist to distinguish between toxic and nontoxic plants.

The Medicinal Use of Plants

Plants are often used to treat a disease or an ailment. For instance, cuts, bruises, and other injuries can be treated with strong anti-inflammatory and quick-healing herbs, such as comfrey (*Symphytum officinale*) or plantain (*Plantago major*) applied as a poultice. Seeds, leaves, stalks, bark, and flowers from a variety of plants and shrubs can be used to treat tummy upsets, fever, dyspepsia, and many other ailments. Plants are also, generally, highly nutritious. They are packed with vitamins, minerals, and other active constituents that can create a positive effect within the body.

The first documentation of the medicinal properties of plants dates back to 1578AD when Shih-Chen Li wrote *An Outline Of Materia Medica*. The Yellow Emperor's *Classics of Internal Medicine*, written over two thousand years ago by herbalists in Nei Ching, is another invaluable source of ancient wisdom. Empirical knowledge—knowledge that is based on experience and observation—has also been handed down from generation to generation within many cultures, and this information is priceless.

The writings of Kuo P'o, a famous Chinese scholar who wrote *Erh Ya* (a dictionary dating from 359AD), includes references to boiling medicinal green leaves, then called k'utu.

The Health Benefits of Tea

It is often said in Chinese literature that foods and medicine share a common source. This is almost certainly the case with tea. It has been proven that the strong antioxidants found in tea are anticancerous. This fact may explain why Asians have the lowest rate of heart disease and cancer in the world, despite a high percentage of heavy smokers among the population.

Tea contains tannins, fluoride, selenium, zinc, flavonols, polyphenols, beta-carotene, and vitamins C and E. It also has an alkaline effect within the body. This alkalinity makes it useful in the treatment of ulcers, or for those who eat too many foods that have an acid-forming reaction in the body, such as meats and dairy products.

The Benefits of Green Tea

Green tea provides the richest health benefits of all teas. It is the most potent, retaining more vitamins and minerals than other teas. Polyphenols, vitamin E, vitamin C, fluoride, quercetin, tannins, and volatile oils work together as strong antioxidants to help the body ward off carcinogenic mutations. Green tea is cooling and cleansing, with low amounts of caffeine, and is rich in vitamins A, B2, C, D, and E, and flavonoids. Green tea helps to reduce cholesterol by lowering blood lipids.

Scientists have proven over the last fifteen years or so, with experiments on mice, that green tea can both prevent and reduce the incidence of stomach and skin cancers. Green tea is thought to be twenty times stronger than vitamin E in its antiaging properties. It reduces free-radical damage and DNA mutation of cells in the body. Green tea is rich in vitamin C and other antioxidants, such as vitamin E and quercetin. Drinking three to four cups a day of this liquid is worth its weight in gold.

Tannins

Tannins are found in the roots, bark, leaves, and fruit of some plants. They have been used for centuries to tan animal hides in making leather. During the tanning process, tannins and protein come into contact with each other, causing the protein cells to curdle and shrink, tightening the skin.

Tannins are present in black tea and, to a lesser extent, green tea. They are complex polyphenols that have an astringent effect on the body. This astringency causes a tightening and drying of skin and mucous membranes. When you drink a strong cup of black tea, you can gauge the strength of the tannins by the fuzzy feeling on your tongue.

There are good and bad elements to tannins. They can stain the teeth after prolonged tea drinking. They may decrease the absorption of vitamins and minerals, as they can "tan" the stomach lining. They can also aggravate constipation. By adding a squeeze of lemon or a dash of milk to tea, however, you can bind the tannins. Milk and lemon cause the tannins to precipitate, making them less effective. On the positive side, it is the tannins that give tea some of its color and taste. Tannins are also useful to control diarrhea, soothe sore red eyes, and treat infections of the mouth and cervix. To get the maximum amount of tannins from tea, it should be steeped for three to five minutes.

Black tea contains about six to eight percent tannins. Green tea contains negligible amounts. As a result, it can be consumed without milk or lemon and will not cause constipation. Oolong contains about 20 percent tannins. Chinese black tea contains about seven percent, and Indian black tea contains about eight percent. Some herbs also contain tannins, with the highest percentage found in Oak bark, which is prescribed internally to tone and heal mucous membranes for those suffering from diarrhea, and externally for weeping eczema and other skin conditions.

Caffeine

Caffeine is an alkaloid found mainly in tea, coffee, and cola drinks, as well as in chocolate, soft drinks, and "sports" drinks made with guarana, a Brazilian cocoa that contains seven percent caffeine and twelve percent tannins. Caffeine has a bitter taste and acts as a stimulant to the central nervous system.

The stimulating effects of caffeine can be harmful if taken in excess. It can increase blood pressure; urine secretions (by 30 percent); acid secretions, resulting in reflux and inflammation in the stomach; heart rate; and breathing. On the other hand, if used sensibly, caffeine can have positive effects, such as increasing alertness, reducing migraine attacks (due to its ability to constrict dilated blood vessels), and widening bronchial airways in asthmatics if the sufferer is not accustomed to caffeine.

Caffeine can also be addictive. Drinking 1/8 ounce (350 mg) of caffeine per day, the equivalent of four cups of coffee or eight cups of black tea, is addictive. Drinking the equivalent of a cup of coffee after eating can interfere with the body's absorption of iron and B vitamins. This decrease in the amounts of nutrients absorbed by the body can increase blood cholesterol and cause insomnia. Pregnant woman who drink 1/4 ounce (650 mg) of caffeine per day can cause serious DNA changes in their unborn child, leading to mutations and defects. The baby may also be born with caffeine dependency.

The caffeine and phosphates in soft drinks flush calcium from bones. Women with menopausal symptoms of bone loss and irritability should totally avoid all products containing caffeine.

Tea contains only half the amount of caffeine that coffee does. The caffeine in tea is known as theophylline and theobromine, which are much milder and gentler stimulants than the caffeine found in coffee and have fewer side effects.

Methods of Brewing

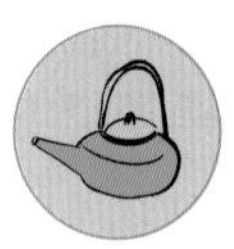

The best tea is made from organically grown plants. The leaves, flowers, roots, or bark should crackle when dry. Tea bags don't usually produce as good a result as loose tea. When buying tea, you can distinguish a good tea leaf from a poor-quality one by smelling it to make sure that there is no mold present and that the tea has a full aroma. Most of the recipes in this book can be made either directly in the cup or in a teapot. Ceramic or glass teapots are preferable, as these materials do not interfere with the flavor of the tea.

The ingredients used to make tea can be bought fresh, dried, or in a powdered form. Some recipes in this book call for the fresh plant to be used. If it is not available, use the dried substitute. **When brewing, bear in mind that, generally, 1 teaspoon of freshly chopped herbs ("herb" refers to the flower, leaf or stem) equals 1/2 teaspoon of the herb dried, or 1/4 teaspoon powdered.** These figures are approximate, and will vary from plant to plant. Experiment to find the flavor you like best.

Infusion

An infusion is where the plant material is placed in a teapot or cup, then boiling water is added. The mixture is allowed to steep so that the flavors are infused into the water. It is best to make an infusion just before drinking it, but you can make enough for the day and then reheat it or drink it cool. Green tea can be reused up to six times, resulting in a new and interesting taste each time.

The parts of plants used most often for infusions are leaves, flowers, stems, roots, and bark. When using dried or fresh herbs, crumble, chop, grind, or slice them to expose as much surface area as possible. This ensures that the maximum amount of the medicinal substances in the herb are drawn into the water.

Most teas require boiling water for infusion. Some Oolong and black teas brew best with near-boiling water. Green and jasmine teas, on the other hand, have a gentler, softer nature, so the flavor is best achieved with water that has been left to stand for 2–3 minutes after boiling. Herbs, such as dandelion root, can be soaked overnight, strained, then drunk the next day. When making infusions, use only filtered or bottled spring water, free of chlorine, fluoride, and other chemical additives. These chemicals affect the taste of the tea. Always cover tea while it is infusing, to keep in the heat and to prevent the loss of aromatic oils through evaporation.

To infuse 2 cups (16 fl oz/500 ml), you will need 1–2 tablespoons of tea leaves or herb. Warm both the teapot and cups. Place the herbs or tea in the teapot. Add 2 cups (16 fl oz/500 ml) boiling water, cover, and let steep for 5–10 minutes. Pour through a strainer, if necessary, into the cups.

To infuse a single cup of tea, use 1 teaspoon of dried herb or tea with 1 cup (8 fl oz/250 ml) of boiling water. Place the herb or tea in a warmed cup or small teapot. Add the boiling water, cover, and let steep for 5–10 minutes.

Unlike herbal tea, green tea should be left to steep for 1 minute only; however, some green teas from Vietnam or India, such as Darjeeling greens, will need up to 6–7 minutes. When buying Asian teas, ask for the steeping time of each tea. In the end it all comes together with practice.

Infusion

Straining

Chinese and Japanese grocery stores sell china teapots with built-in strainers. These pots are ideal for the recipes in this book. The measured dried herb is placed in the strainer, boiling water is poured over, and then it is all left to steep. This makes it simpler to pour hot water over the leaves throughout the day to make fresh brews. This is especially good when brewing your favorite green tea. To make just one cup, you can use a cup-size strainer. Simply place the strainer in the cup, and pour boiling water over until the strainer is fully covered.

Straining

Decoction

Twigs, stems, barks, and roots can be decocted, which means simmering them to extract their flavors and medicinal constituents. The cooking times will vary depending on the type and quantity of plant used. The recipes in this book indicate the time required, but you may prefer to experiment with times to find the strength you prefer. This method does not allow for the reuse of the tea, as it extracts all the flavor and goodness during decoction.

To decoct 2 cups (16 fl oz/500 ml), you will need 2–3 tablespoons of the plant. Place it in a saucepan, add 2 cups of water, and bring to a boil over a medium-high heat. Reduce heat to medium-low, cover, and simmer for 15–20 minutes, or until reduced by one-third. Strain into a cup, then drink while hot.

Decoction

Ingredients

If the fresh ingredient is out of season or otherwise unavailable, use the dried substitute. Generally, one teaspoon of chopped fresh herb equals 1/2 teaspoon of the dried herb. If the recipe calls for dried herb, you can substitute the fresh alternative. Use approximately double the amount of fresh herb. For some plants, if the flavor is mild you can use a little more than double the amount of dried herb. Note that "herb" refers to the aerial (above ground) part of the plant: the flower, leaf, and stem.

CHINESE TEAS
Orange Pekoe tea leaves
Oolong
Lychee
Souchong
Keemun
Chunmee
Jasmine Pearl
Gunpowder
Spearmint
Lung Ching
Pai Mu Tan

INDIAN TEAS
Darjeeling
Assam
Nilgiri
Ceylon

JAPANESE TEAS
Matcha Uji powder
Bancha
Houjicha
Sencha
Gyokuru

Alfalfa seeds
(Medicago sativa)

Angelica root
(Angelica archangelica)

Aniseed
(Pimpinella anisum)

Astragalus root (dried)
(Astragalus membranaceus)

Bilberry
(Vaccinium myrtilis)

Black cohosh root
(Cimicifuga racemosa)

Black currants
(Ribes nigrum)

Buchu leaves
(Barosima betulina)

Calendula flowers (dried)
(Calendula officinalis)

Cardamom pods
(Elattaria cardamomum)

Chamomile flowers (dried)
(Matracaria recutita)

Chickweed herb
(Stellaria media)

Chrysanthemum flowers (dried)
(Chrysanthemum x morifolium)

Cinnamon stick
(Cinnamomum verum)

Clivers
(Galium aparine)

Cloves
(Syzygium aromaticum)

Corn silk
(Zea mays)

Dandelion leaf
Dandelion root (dried)
(Taraxacum radix)

Echinacea
(Echinacea purpurea/angustifolia)

Elderberries
Elderberry flowers (dried)
(Sambucus nigra)

Elecampane root (dried)
(Inula helenium)

Eyebright herb
(Euphrasia officinalis)

Fennel seed
(Foeniculum officinale)

Ginger root
(Zingiber officianalis)

Gotu kola leaves
(Centella asciatica)

Hawthorn berries
(Crataegus spp)

Hibiscus calyces (outer coverings of flower bud)
(Rosa seninsis)

Honeysuckle flowers
(Lonicera japonica)

Hop strobiles
(Humulus lupulus)

Horehound flowers
(Marribum vulgare)

Juniper berries
(Juniperus communis)

Korean ginseng
Korean ginseng (dried)
(Panax Ginseng)

Lavender flowers/leaves
(Lavendula angustifolia)

Lemon balm leaves (dried)
(Melissa officinalis)

Lemongrass
Lemongrass (dried)
(Cymbogon citratus)

Licorice root
(Glyccyrrhiza glabra)

Lime blossom
(Tilia europea)

Mallow flowers/leaves
(Malva sylvestris)

Marshmallow flower/leaf/root
(Althaea officinalis)

Meadowsweet flowers and leaves
(Filipendula ulmaria)

Mullein flowers/leaves/seeds
(Verbascum thapsus)

Nettle
(Urtica diocia)

Oat straw
(Avena sativa)

Passionflower
(Passiflora incarnata)

Peppermint leaves
(Mentha x piperita)

Raspberry leaf (dried)
(Rubus idaeus)

Red clover
(Trifolium pratense)

Ribwort (Plantain) leaf
(Plantago major)

Rose petals
(Rosa spp)

Rosemary leaves
(Rosmarinus officinalis)

Sage
Sage (dried)
(Salvia officinalis)

Siberian ginseng root (dried and sliced)
(Eleutherococcus senticosus)

Skullcap herb
(Scutellaria lateriflora)

St. John's wort
(Hypericum perforatum)

Thyme
Thyme (dried)
(Thymus vulgarus)

Uva ursi leaf
(Arctostophylos uva-ursi)

Valerian root
(Valeriana officinalis)

Vervain herb
(Verbena officinalis)

Vitex berries
(Vitex agnus-castus)

Yarrow
Yarrow (dried)
(Achellia millefolium)

CHINA CHOICE
OOLONG TEA
祺棧茶行
KI CHAN TEA CO.
174 JOHNSTON ROAD, H.K.
TEL: 25730690 25732042
TRADE MARK
CHINA GREEN TEA
LUNG CHING
白猴鐵觀音

Teas from China

~

Orange Pekoe Tea

Orange Pekoe comes from Shanghai and has a mild, yet smoky, flavor. In reputable gardens, depending upon how the tea leaves are rolled, the whole leaf, between 1/3–2/3 inch (8–15 mm) long, is known as Orange Pekoe. Tippy Golden Flowery Orange Pekoe has leaves with a golden tip. Golden Flowery Orange Pekoe has only some leaves with golden tips . Flowery Pekoe has a length of 1/5–1/3 inch (5–8 mm). Other varieties include Pekoe, Pekoe Souchong, Souchong and Eshan.

Broken grades make up 95 percent of Orange Pekoe production. They are in higher demand because, due to their size, they produce the best brewing tea. Varieties include Broken Orange Pekoe and Broken Pekoe.

Eshan Pekoe Tea

This tea comes from a town called Eshan in the Yunnan province. It has a strong flavor and is often served on special occasions.

Makes 2 cups (16 fl oz/500 ml)
serves 4–5

boiling water for warming
1–2 teaspoons Eshan tea leaves
2 cups (16 fl oz/500 ml) boiling water

Fill a ceramic or glass teapot with boiling water, cover, and let stand for 1 minute to warm. Fill the teacups with boiling water and set aside to warm.

Drain the water from the teapot. Put the tea leaves in the pot and fill with the boiling water. Cover and let steep for 1 minute.

Empty the water from the cups. Pour the tea into the cups and drink it hot. You can repeat the refilling and pouring several times by boiling more water and reusing the tea leaves.

Oolong Tea

Oolong comes from Taiwan (formerly Formosa), where the climate is perfect for tea growing: the humidity is 92 percent for most of the year. The tea grows on small plantations that are not open to the public because the growers are secretive about the production.

Oolong is semi-fermented. It has the taste and color of half-green, half-black tea. Ti-Kuan-Yin, also known as The Goddess, is grown in northern Formosa and is said to rid the body of toxins and all its ills. Black Dragon is a dark, full-bodied, earthy tea, and High Mountain Oolong has a deep-green leaf that makes a fresh, revitalizing brew used medicinally for indigestion, slimming, and to lower cholesterol. Other varieties include Pu-erh and Oolong Shue Hsein.

Oolong is traditionally brewed in a Gung Fu tea set. The set consists of a small teapot and tiny cups. Only one type of tea is served in any given teapot because as the teapot ages, the flavor seeps into the clay. When the pot is older, all you need to do is add water to taste the tea.

Serving Gung Fu tea is an act of delicacy in itself. The tea is served smoothly and slowly, with grace and elegance.

Far Right: Oolong Tea
Right: Gung Fu Tea

Gung Fu Tea

Makes 1 cup (8 fl oz/250 ml)
or 6–7 Gung Fu teacups

boiling water to warm
1 teaspoon Oolong tea leaves
1 cup (8 fl oz/250 ml) boiling water

Fill a ceramic or glass teapot with boiling water, cover, and let stand for 2 minutes to warm. Fill the teacups with boiling water and set aside to warm.

Drain the water from the teapot. Put the tea leaves in the pot, then rinse with boiling water and drain, retaining the tea leaves. Immediately fill the teapot with the cup of boiling water, cover, and let steep for 30 seconds to 2 minutes.

Empty the water from the cups. Strain the tea into the cups and drink. You can refill the pot with water 3–5 times. Each brew will produce a different flavor.

Black Lychee Tea

This exotic tea, sweetened with lychee fruit from southern China, is very popular. The leaf has a distinct fine texture and mellow taste. It is made from the finest Chinese tea leaves, cured in rooms filled with steaming lychees. This creates a sensational taste: heavy-bodied, sweet, and slightly fruity. It is excellent served on hot, steamy days as an iced tea.

Makes 2 cups (16 fl oz/500 ml)
or 4–5 Chinese teacups

2 teaspoons lychee tea leaves
2 cups (16 fl oz/500 ml) boiling water

Put the lychee tea leaves in a warmed ceramic or glass teapot. Add boiling water, cover and let steep for 2 minutes. Strain into cups and drink hot. More boiling water can be added to the remaining tea leaves to make 1 or 2 more infusions.

Souchong Tea

Souchong is a whole-leaf black tea made from dark leaves that are large and thick. Souchong was originally grown in the Fujian province and was known by the Chinese as Tarry Souchong. Its special characteristics are due to the soil in which it is grown.

Taiwan (formerly Formosa) produces Lapsong Souchong, which is loved for the smoky flavor developed during the curing process. The leaves are pan-fired over aromatic open fires of pine. Lapsong Souchong means "the largest leaf." The taste is mildly spicy, heavy-bodied, and rich, with a smoky flavor. The leaves are grown high in the Wu Yi Mountains, which are full of heavy mist and dense pine forests. This honey-colored tea enhances the appetite and stimulates digestion.

Souchong goes perfectly with savory and spicy foods, such as cheese and olives.

Makes 2 cups (16 fl oz/500 ml)
or 4–5 Chinese teacups

2 teaspoons Souchong tea leaves
2 cups (16 fl oz/500 ml) boiling water

Put the tea leaves in a warmed ceramic or glass teapot. Add the boiling water, cover, and let steep for 1 minute. Strain into Chinese teacups and drink hot.

***Left:* Lychees**

Keemun Tea

This is a mild black tea that grows in aromatic orchards in the Anhui and Jiangxi provinces. It is famous for the bright-red tea it produces. The mild, sweet infusion it brews makes it a pleasant tea to have almost anytime. Due to its mild, sweet taste, Keemun tea is often used in China as a base for other scented teas. It is rich in minerals, which give it a unique color, flavor, and aroma. Keemun tea can be drunk to relieve fever and as a preventative to cancer.

Not many people get to see the finest tea plantations in China, known as the "sacred gardens." They remain a secret even from the Chinese themselves. A few estates are believed to be guarded by security dogs both day and night. High-quality standard teas, such as Imperial Yunnan from Southern China and Imperial Keemun from the Anhui Mountains, are designed for export. Keemun Finest, exported from the Jiangxi province, has a tiny, delicate leaf that produces a tea with a mildly nutty flavor.

Makes 2 cups (16 fl oz/500 ml)
or 4–5 Chinese tea cups

2 teaspoons Keemun Finest tea leaves
2 cups (16 fl oz/500 ml) boiling water

Put the tea leaves in a warmed ceramic or glass teapot. Add the boiling water, cover, and let steep for 1–2 minutes. Strain into cups and drink hot.

***Right:* Keemun Tea**

Chunmee Tea

Chunmee is well known all over the world as Green China tea. Its Chinese name means "precious eyebrow," because of the shape of the leaf. It is grown high in the Yunnan province. The leaf is processed into a hard, slender, slightly coarse, twisted roll, about 3/8 inch (1 cm) in length.

Infused, Chunmee is light in color, with a distinct fruity taste similar to plum. It needs only light brewing and will make a number of tasty infusions. It has the ability to quench thirst, improve digestion, have a positive effect on eyesight, and raise spirits. It is the most produced green tea in China as well as being the most heavily exported.

Makes 2 cups (16 fl oz/500 ml)
serves 4–5 Chinese teacups

1–2 teaspoons Chunmee tea leaves
2 cups (16 fl oz/500 ml) boiling water

Put the tea leaves in a warmed ceramic or glass teapot. Add the water and let steep for 2–3 minutes. Strain into Chinese teacups and drink hot.

Jasmine Tea

The finest jasmine teas comes from China. Freshly cut blossoms of jasmine are added to green tea to give it a distinct and glorious aroma. This can happen only at night, when the jasmine flower opens. The flowers and buds are placed over the tea on bamboo trays and removed in the morning. Fresh buds and flowers are added the following night. This process is repeated up to ten times, until the scent is embedded in the tea. Most flowers and petals are removed after the scenting process, but sometimes they are retained, as in Jasmine Flower and Jasmine Pearl.

Jasmine Pearl tea contains the whole blossom or bud. It is fragrant and strong, and is scented by the tender jasmine bud. The tea leaves and buds are rolled into pearl-like balls that open on steeping.

Makes 2 cups (16 fl oz/500 ml)
or 4–5 Chinese teacups

2 cups (16 fl oz/500 ml) boiling water
2 teaspoons Jasmine Pearl tea leaves

Allow the boiling water to cool slightly. Put the tea leaves in a warmed ceramic or glass teapot. Add the water, cover, and let steep for 30–60 seconds. Pour into teacups and drink hot.

***Right:** Jasmine Tea*

Gunpowder Tea

This is a popular green tea in China. Gunpowder leaves are rolled into small balls, up to 1/8 inch (3 mm) wide, and are mixed with the finest mint teas from Africa and the Near East. The tiny balls of green tea explode in hot water and sink, releasing a yellow–green infusion that is very refreshing with mint. Gunpowder leaves on their own taste slightly bitter, strong, astringent, and smoky.

Different types of Gunpowder tea include Gunpowder (Xiao Qiu), a leaf that makes a dark-green infusion with a strong, long-lasting taste, and Gunpowder Pinhead Temple of Heaven, a tiny premium Gunpowder grade of leaf that can be brewed in many infusions.

Gunpowder and Spearmint tea is commonly drunk in Morocco as a sweet digestive. It has a clean, refreshing aftertaste.

Makes 2 cups (16 fl oz/500 ml)
or 4–5 Chinese teacups

1–2 teaspoons Gunpowder tea leaves
1–2 teaspoons dried spearmint tea leaves
2 cups (16 fl oz/500 ml) boiling water
honey to taste (optional)

Put the tea leaves in a warmed ceramic or glass teapot. Add the boiling water, cover, and let steep for 1–3 minutes. Stir in honey to sweeten, if desired.

Lung Ching Tea

The Zhejiang province is famous for this outstanding tea. Its name means "Dragon's Well." Lung Ching is one of the world's finest, rarest, and most expensive green teas. It can only be bought through a special agreement with the right authorities.

Lung Ching makes a jade-colored infusion with a subtle aroma and charming flavor. It is known to be stimulating and good for keeping the mind alert and clear on late nights. Lung Ching is considered a prestigious and special gift; it is sometimes given to a bride and groom on their wedding day (usually one pack for each).

Makes 2 cups (16 fl oz/500 ml)
or 4–5 Chinese teacups

2 teaspoons Lung Ching tea leaves
2 cups (16 fl oz/500 ml) boiling water

Put the tea in a warmed ceramic or glass teapot. Add the water, cover, and let steep for 30 seconds–2 minutes. Strain, then drink hot.

Right: Gunpowder Tea

White Chinese Tea

White Chinese tea, also known as Mutant White, White Peony tea, and Pai Mu Tan, is one of the rarest teas. It is also expensive. It is produced in the Fujian province, and is only harvested on a few days of the year. Studies performed in America show that white tea may be more potent than green tea when it comes to treating cancer, particularly colon cancer. White teas are fluffy and light. When brewing a white tea, you will need to add more tea leaves than for black or green teas. The liquor it provides is pale and golden in color, mellow in taste.

Mutant White or White Peony tea is made from Dai Bai, or Big White tea leaves, and can be mixed with White Peony buds. The buds have a silver tip and are covered in down. They look beautiful as they stand upright in the teapot, producing a pale orange-yellow infusion.

Makes 2 cups (16 fl oz/500 ml)
or 4–5 Chinese teacups

4 teaspoons White Peony tea leaves
2 cups (16 fl oz/500 ml) boiling water

Put the tea leaves in a warmed ceramic or glass teapot. Add the water, cover, and let steep for 2 minutes. Strain, then drink hot.

Bac Thai Tea

Some tea connoisseurs believe Vietnam could be the birthplace of tea. The bushes that grow in its valleys are small-leafed and sweet. Bac Thai is a common tea in Vietnam and is sold at Asian grocery stores elsewhere. It is favored in hot and humid areas because of its cooling effect on the body. The tea is yellow when steeped and suitable to drink all day long on hot summer days. Bac Thai is a smooth and delightful tea.

Makes 2 cups (16 fl oz/500 ml)
or 4–5 Chinese teacups

1–2 teaspoons Bac Thai tea leaves
2 cups (16 fl oz/500 ml) boiling water

Put the tea in a warmed ceramic or glass teapot. Add water, cover, and let steep for 2–3 minutes. Strain, then drink hot.

Right: White Chinese Tea

Teas from India

~

Darjeeling Tea

The Darjeeling region of India borders Nepal. At dawn, Himalayn women set off to pick the leaves of this tea variety that is considered the champagne of teas. The precious tea leaves are grown at altitudes of 6500 feet (1,970 meters). The plantations can produce 15,000 tons of tea a year, which is harvested according to traditional methods. Compared with other teas, Darjeeling is delicate, soft, and tender. Its popularity stems from its aromatic flavor and astringency.

Makes 2 cups (16 fl oz/500 ml)
serves 2–3

2 teaspoons black or green Darjeeling tea leaves
2 cups (16 fl oz/500 ml) boiling water

Put the tea leaves in a warmed ceramic or glass teapot. Add the water, cover, and let steep for 3–5 minutes for black tea, or 30–60 seconds for green tea.

Spicy Himalayan Tea

This hot and spicy tea goes well with sweets after dinner. It is known in India as Garam Himalaya chai.

Makes 4 cups (32 fl oz/1 L)
serves 5–6

1 bay leaf
1/2 tablespoon fennel seeds or aniseed
3 tablespoons packed brown sugar or honey
3 cardamom pods
6 cloves
1 cinnamon stick
1/4 teaspoon black peppercorns
1 teaspoon peeled and grated fresh ginger
3 1/2 cups (28 fl oz/875 ml) water
2 tablespoons Darjeeling tea leaves
1/2 cup (4 fl oz/125 ml) milk

Combine all the ingredients except the tea leaves and milk in a saucepan. Bring to a boil over high heat. Reduce heat to low, cover, and simmer for 20 minutes. Add the tea leaves, remove from heat, and let steep for 10 minutes.

Add the milk and brint to a boil over medium heat. Strain, then drink hot.

Left: Cardamom pods and cinnamon sticks

Assam Tea

The Assam Valley is 75 miles (120 km) east of Darjeeling, on the Chinese, Burmese, and Bangladesh borders. The valley was once dense jungle, but it was cleared by the English in the early 1800s. This is one of the wettest regions in the world. Every year, monsoons cause the river banks to burst, flooding the region. There are two hundred tea plantations in Assam, which yield a third of all the tea produced in India.

Only the very best leaves are plucked—the terminal bud, when it is covered in white down, and the two leaves below it—for Assam tea. (It is said that only the slender fingers of a woman can accomplish successful high-grade plucking.) The Assam tea bush, *Thea assamica*, is similar to the Chinese tea plant. The black teas of the region are grown for intensity, and are strong, flavorful teas. Only a few are grown for green tea, but the green teas produced here develop a taste that is piquant and preferred by the new green tea drinker.

Makes 1 cup (8 fl oz/250 ml)
serves 1

1/2–1 teaspoon Assam tea leaves
1 cup (8 fl oz/250 ml) boiling water
milk and sugar or honey, if desired

Place the tea leaves in a warmed small ceramic or glass teapot or cup. Add water and let steep for 1–2 minutes. Strain into a cup, add milk and sweetener, if desired. Drink hot.

Assam Cardamom Tea

Cardamom pods add a special touch to Assam tea. Cardamom is used in many foods to flavor and add a bit of an edge. This tasty tea is refreshing and cooling to drink.

Makes 4 cups (32 fl oz/1 L)
serves 5–6

3 1/2 cups (28 fl oz/875 ml) water
6 green cardamom pods
1 tablespoon Assam tea leaves
1/2 cup (4 fl oz/125 ml) milk
1/4 cup (2 oz/60 g) packed brown sugar or honey

Put the water in a saucepan and bring to a boil over medium heat. Add the cardamom, cover, and boil for 3–5 minutes. Remove from heat, cover, and let steep for 5 minutes. Add the tea leaves, bring to a boil and boil for 3 minutes. Add the milk and sweetener. Strain and drink piping hot.

***Right:* Assam Tea**

Nilgiri Tea

Unlike teas from Assam and Darjeeling, Nilgiri grows year- round. It is known locally as the fragrant tea and is ideal for mixing with other varieties. Its intense and aromatic flavor makes excellent exotic flower or fruit blends. Nilgiri green teas are delicate and can be enjoyed all day.

People living in the cooler regions of India tend to enjoy spiced teas. The spices act as a circulatory stimulant, warming and nurturing the body. Indian Spiced Nilgiri tea is delightfully fragrant and is known in India as Masalewali chai.

Makes 3 cups (24 fl oz/750 ml)
serves 4–5

3 1/2 cups (28 fl oz/875 ml) water
1/2 cup milk
1 tablespoon Nilgiri tea leaves
1 teaspoon peeled and grated fresh ginger
1 cinnamon stick
3 green cardamom pods
3 cloves
1 tablespoon packed brown sugar or honey

Combine the water and milk in a saucepan and bring to a boil over a medium heat. Add the spices and sweetener and boil for 5 minutes. Turn off heat, cover, and let steep for 10 minutes. Add the tea leaves, cover, and return to a boil. Reduce heat to low and simmer for 7 minutes. Strain, then drink hot.

Ceylon Tea

In the beautiful rolling hills of Sri Lanka are smaller tea plantations where tea preferred by Americans and Europeans is grown. Over 600 million pounds (272 million kg) of tea is grown here each year. The best Ceylon teas, such as Uva, Kandy, and Nuwara Eliya, come from the higher altitudes. Varieties of Ceylon tea include Ceylon Orange Pekoe, from the high district; Ceylon Cottaganga, which is organic; Dotel Oya Oop and Aislaby Pekoe, from the Uva District; Pettiagalla Op and Matale Curly Pekoe, from the Dimbula District; and Battalgalla Op and Lovers Leap Bop, from the Nuwara Eliya District.

Makes 1 cup (8 fl oz/250 ml)
serves 1

1 teaspoon Ceylon tea leaves
1 cup (8 fl oz/250 ml) boiling water
Milk or lemon, if desired

Put the tea leaves in a warmed small ceramic or glass teapot or cup. Add the water, cover, and let steep for 3–5 minutes. Strain, then drink hot with milk or lemon, if you like.

Right:* *Nilgiri Tea

Teas from Japan

~

Japan produces only green teas, which are grown on Mount Fuji, in Schizuoka, and on the island of Kyusu. The Japanese tea leaf is greener and brighter in color than its Chinese counterpart, as is the tea it makes. The flavor of Japanese green teas is also usually stronger than that of Chinese green teas. Japanese green tea is very high in vitamin C and is a great digestive before and after meals.

Tea Ceremonies

The Japanese have created a wonderful ritual around the drinking of tea. Japanse tea ceremonies are called *chado* or *sado*, which means "way of tea." They are also known as Cha-No-Yu, meaning "hot water tea" (Cha means "tea".)

The ceremony is a ritual created by Zen Buddhist priests over several centuries. It is founded on the appreciation of life and daily routine. The priests first practiced the ceremony during the Kamakura Period in Japan (1192–1333). After discovering that tea helped them to stay alert during meditation, the priests made it part of their daily lives. Later it became part of Zen rituals in honor of Bodhidharma, the founder of Zen Buddhism.

The tea ceremony was refined to the discipline we know today mainly by three Zen monks in the 12th, 13th and 14th centuries: Ikkyu (1394–1481), a former prince; Murata Shuko (1422–1502), Ikkyu's student; and Sen no Rikyu (1521–1591), who introduced it to the military; it then became customary for the soldiers to attend a tea ceremony before going into battle.

Sen and his followers gave the tea ceremony a style known as *wabi*, meaning "quiet, simplicity and absence of ornament." *Wabi* emphasizes four important points:

1. harmony between guests and implements;
2. respect for others present and for the utensils;
3. cleanliness (a Shinto practice that involves washing your hands and rinsing your mouth before entering the teahouse); and
4. tranquility, which is emphasized throughout the ceremony by the slow, delicate care that is applied to each article used during the ceremony.

Sen's love for the tea ceremony made it what it is today. He was a great man who introduced an art, philosophy and pleasure to drinking tea.

Chanoyu

The tea ceremony, Chanoyu, takes place in a teahouse (*cha-shitsu*), a small building detached from the rest of the house. Most teahouses are 10 feet (3 meters) square, with an alcove (*toko-no-mo*) holding a scroll. There may also be a flower arrangement or one single flower instead of the alcove. There is usually a painting, and a fireplace (*ro*) to heat the kettle on, as well as a mat (*tatami*) on the floor. The door leading into the room is low, so guests need to bow. This makes them all equal in the eyes of each other.

Guests are seated and the tea utensils are brought into the room by the host. All those present focus on the tea and its creation. This is done to create an atmosphere of relaxation, free from worry. The idea is to teach precision, poise, equanimity, kindness, sincerity, and generosity, resulting in harmony for all. The host brings in sweets, usually made from red bean paste. A sweet is offered to each guest to eat with his or her tea.

Left: Matcha Uji powder and implements for tea ceremony

Matcha Uji

The leaves used for a tea ceremony are a fine-quality green tea known as Matcha. It is made from Japan's finest tea, Gyokuru. It is dried, then ground very finely. The expensive leaves are gently stirred into hot water with refinement and elegance until a frothy consistency is reached. On some occasions, a heavier tea is brewed, called Koicha. A bowl is then gracefully placed in front of each guest, to be held with both hands and sipped. When the tea is finished and the sweets are eaten, guests can ask questions pertaining to the ceremony.

Matcha Uji means 'froth of liquid jade.' Gyokuro tea leaves are steamed and spread flat to dry. The leaves are then ground to a powder as fine as talc. This exquisite tea creates a jade-green infusion that is nourishing and full-bodied. The tea is made directly in a warmed small bowl and makes a nice accompaniment to Japanese sweets. When the tea is whisked with a dampened bamboo stick, it becomes frothy. Matcha Uji is often used to color other foods and make iced tea. The frothier the tea is, the less astringent and bitter it will be.

Note: When brewing green teas, never use a strainer or tea ball. The leaf needs to be relaxed, or loose, so it can unfold, open up, and release all its flavor. While some teas become lighter and milder with each brew, others become richer and fuller.

Makes 1/5 cup (1 fl oz/50 ml)
serves 1

1/5 cup (1 fl oz/50 ml) boiling water
1/2–1 teaspoon Matcha Uji powder

Let the water stand for 1–2 minutes to cool slightly. Put the tea powder in a small, warmed bowl. Add the water and use a whisk to stir briskly until frothy. Drink by taking three long sips and then pause. Repeat until the bowl is empty.

Right: Matcha Uji

Bancha

This long, flat tea leaf makes a mild, refreshing green tea. Bancha means "late harvest." It is produced for everyday use in Japan. Considered common and rough, it is mixed with stems and other low-grade green teas. Served with meals as a digestive, Bancha is bitter and slightly astringent. It can also be served with sake.

Makes 2 cups (16 fl oz/500 ml)
or 4–5 Japanese teacups

2 cups (16 fl oz/500 ml) boiling water
2 tablespoons Bancha tea leaves

Let the water stand for 1–2 minutes to cool slightly. Put the tea leaves in a warmed teapot. Add water and let steep for 2–3 minutes. Strain, then drink hot. Pour all the tea at once so the leaves don't steep any longer. The leaves can be reinfused to make another pot of tea.

Houjicha

Houjicha was invented long ago in an attempt to improve on the taste of Bancha. Its name means "a grilled tea leaf," and it is also known as Roasted Bancha. Houjicha tea leaves are originally green before being roasted to a brown color. The tea it produces is light in flavor, reddish-brown in color, and tastes nutty. The flavor actually resembles coffee more than tea.

Houjicha is a good tea to serve with a meal, especially with savory foods such as sushi and sashimi. Its caffeine content is very low, so it can also be drunk at night. This versatile tea can be drunk hot, warm or cool, but not cold. If you are concerned with nutrients, however, you should know that the vitamins and minerals in this tea are destroyed during roasting.

Makes 2 cups (16 fl oz/500 ml)
or 4–5 Japanese teacups

2 teaspoons Houjicha tea leaves
2 cups (16 fl oz/500 ml) boiling water

Put the tea leaves in a teapot. Add the water and let steep for 2–3 minutes. Strain, then drink hot, warm, or cool.

Right: Houjicha

Sencha

Sencha tea uses whole, unrolled leaves. The Sencha leaf has a needlelike shape. It comes in many different grades, which are all delicious in their own right. Sencha teas are now being produced by China and Vietnam for export to Japan. Sencha Honyama stands out from the rest. It produces a fresh and flowery infusion that is perfect to enjoy on a relaxing afternoon. Sencha tea is made in a special Kyusu teapot, which has a handle that is perpendicular to the spout.

Makes 1/2 cup (4 fl oz/125 ml)
or 4–5 small Kyusu teacups

1/2 cup (4 fl oz/120 ml) boiling water
2 teaspoons Sencha tea leaves

Let the water stand for 1–2 minutes to cool slightly. Meanwhile, fill the teapot with hot water, cover, and let stand for 1 minute to warm. Drain the water. Put the tea leaves in the teapot. Add the water and let steep for 1 minute only. Strain, then drink hot. You can reinfuse this tea a couple of times.

Gyokuro Tea

This is one of Japan's finest green teas. Grown in beautifully landscaped plantations, the precious tea trees are protected in winter from frost by hot-air fans. As soon as buds appear, bamboo mats are laid over all the trees to stop most of the light getting through. This makes the leaves lower in tannin. The tea infusion is fragrant and dark-green in color, with a smooth, mellow taste.

Makes 1/2 cup (4 fl oz/125 ml)
or 4–5 Kyusu teacups

1/2 cup (4 fl oz/125 ml) boiling water
1 teaspoon Gyokuru tea leaves

Let the water stand for 1–2 minutes to cool slightly. Put the tea leaves in a warmed ceramic or glass teapot. Add the water and let steep for 1 1/2 minutes. Pour into cups immediately and drink while hot. This tea can be reinfused with slightly hotter water.

Right: Sencha

Herbal Teas for Energy

There can be a number of reasons why someone feels a lack of energy. It can be caused by constantly working for too many hours without respite, by dietary or alcohol abuse, by heavy periods for women, by underlying illnesses, or by simply not getting enough sleep. Sometimes this lack of energy can be insidious, creeping up so slowly and gradually that we don't realize it is occurring until the effects are quite dramatic.

Years of dietary abuse can result in what is called, naturopathically (i.e., referring to the terms of natural therapy), malnutrition. Although someone may be eating enough food, quite often they carry too much weight. And it's the quality of food that is eaten, not the quantity, that counts. Many people eat a large amount of fast food, which is high in fat and devoid of the good nutrients, vitamins and minerals found in fresh fruit and vegetables.

People who drink too much coffee and high-caffeine soft drinks, or eat too many chocolates, tend to feel a lack of energy due to caffeine addiction. Caffeine tends to "kick-start" the adrenal glands, which gives an initial burst of energy, but gradually tires the adrenal glands. Ongoing stress can have exactly the same effect on the adrenal glands. Over the years it can be like jump-starting a car with a dead battery. Eventually, it becomes exhausted.

We all need energy, and if it is lacking, life can be miserable. The tea recipes in this chapter are safe, gentle, and effective. However, if you find after trying them for a few weeks that your energy levels have not improved, it would be well worth seeing your health care provider for a thorough assessment.

Left: Valerian and Chamomile Tea

Valerian and Chamomile Tea

Energy depletion can be caused by constant stress. Valerian and chamomile will assist in helping you to relax. Neither of these herbs will make you drowsy; nor will they affect mental alertness. For the best results, drink this tea after work and again just before you go to bed. It can also be drunk at any time during the day. Note that Valerian has a strong taste and smell.

Makes 1 cup (8 fl oz/250 ml)
serves 1

1/2 teaspoon dried valerian root
1/2 teaspoon dried chamomile flowers
1 cup (8 fl oz/250 ml) boiling water
honey (optional)

Combine the valerian and chamomile in a warmed small ceramic or glass teapot or cup. Add the boiling water, cover, and let steep for 5–10 minutes. Strain, then drink while it is hot or allow it to cool first. At bedtime, you can sweeten this tea with 1 teaspoon of honey for a great nightcap.

Skullcap, Dandelion, and Cinnamon Tea

Yang and yin are important concepts in Chinese medicine. Yang tonics treat exhaustion and chronic weakness; yin solutions balance that state by providing nourishment and moisture to the internal organs. Lack of energy, feeling cold, irritability, nervousness, and a loss of sex drive are symptoms of yang deficiency. Alcohol abuse can lead to a severe yang deficiency. Cinnamon increases yang by increasing blood circulation and warming the body. This tea nourishes the liver and mind. Drink it twice a day.

Makes 1 cup (8 fl oz/250 ml)
serves 1

1 teaspoon dried dandelion root
1/2 teaspoon dried skullcap herb
pinch of ground cinnamon
1 cup (8 fl oz/250 ml) boiling water

Combine the dandelion, scullcap, and cinnamon in a warmed small ceramic or glass teapot or cup. Add the boiling water, cover, and let steep for 10 minutes. Pour through a strainer and drink.

Siberian Ginseng, Nettle, and Licorice Tea

If you are always on the go, with a hectic schedule, a demanding job, and family pressures, you should make lifestyle changes to alleviate your energy-sapping stress. This tea will help pick you up in no time. You should notice the effects after a week or two. Licorice has a natural, sweet flavor that makes a pleasant-tasting tea.

Makes 2 cups (16 fl oz/500 ml)
serves 2–3

1 tablespoon dried nettle herb
1 tablespoon dried licorice root
1 tablespoon dried Siberian ginseng root
2 cups (16 fl oz/500 ml) boiling water

Combine the nettle, licorice, and Siberian ginseng in a warmed ceramic or glass teapot. Add the boiling water, cover, and let steep for 10 minutes. Strain and then drink 1 cup every 3 hours or so. If you omit the Siberian ginseng because it is not available, this tea will still be a good general pick-me-up.

Alfalfa, Nettle, and Licorice Tea

Many women lack energy just after a period. This can be caused by insufficient iron in the body. Foods rich in iron should be eaten around this time. Alfalfa, nettle, and licorice are rich in iron, and they make an excellent tea. Licorice is also known as an adaptogen by herbalists because it is a restorative and supportive tonic for the adrenal glands.

Makes 2 cups (16 fl oz/500 ml)
serves 2–3

1 tablespoon alfalfa seeds
2 teaspoons dried nettle herb
1 tablespoon dried licorice root
2 cups (16 fl oz/500 ml) boiling water

Combine the alfalfa, nettle, and licorice in a warmed ceramic or glass teapot. Add the boiling water, cover, and let steep for 10–15 minutes. Strain, then drink during the day.

Red Clover, Hops, and Black Cohosh Tea

During menopause, women can suffer hot flushes, night sweats, and a lack of energy and interest. This tea will help the energy levels. I would also recommend a diet high in soy—tofu, miso soup, tempeh, and non-genetically modified soy milk—and foods rich in phytoestrogens, such as parsley (tabbouleh is the best source), and real licorice or licorice tea.

Makes 2 cups (16 fl oz/500 ml)
serves 2–3

2 teaspoons dried red clover
1 teaspoon dried crushed hop strobiles
1 teaspoon dried black cohosh root
2 cups (16 fl oz/500 ml) boiling water

Put the red clover, hop strobiles and black cohosh in a warmed ceramic or glass teapot. Add the boiling water, cover, and let steep for 10–15 minutes. Strain, then drink 1 cup every 3 to 4 hours. Drink one full teapot each day.

Korean Ginseng, Ginger, and Lavender Tea

Some people, as they grow older, feel they are losing their "get up and go." This tea will help put the sparkle back in the eyes, and a spring back in the step, and will help provide a zest for living once again. Korean ginseng is a pleasant- tasting herb. Ginger is hot and spicy, and is a great tonic on cooler days. Lavender is aromatic and mild, as delicate as it smells.

Makes 1 cup (8 fl oz/250 ml)
serves 1

1 teaspoon granulated Korean ginseng
1/2 teaspoon peeled and grated fresh ginger
1/2 teaspoon chopped fresh lavender flowers
1 cup (8 fl oz/250 ml) boiling water

Combine the ginseng, ginger, and lavender in a warmed small ceramic or glass teapot or cup. Add the boiling water, cover, and let steep for 5 minutes. Strain, then drink hot.

Note: Honey can be added to this tea if desired.

Calendula and Yarrow Tea

Calendula flowers (pot marigold) and yarrow have powerful healing qualities. Both help to strengthen and heal body tissues, and yarrow also acts as a tonic for blood vessels. Both the fresh flowers and the leaves of yarrow can be used. The bright colors of these herbs create a delightful color in a glass teapot.

Makes 2 cups (16 fl oz/500 ml)
serves 2–3

3 tablespoons chopped fresh calendula flowers
2 tablespoons chopped fresh yarrow herb
2 cups (16 fl oz/500 ml) boiling water

Combine the calendula and yarrow in a warmed ceramic or glass teapot. Add the boiling water, cover, and let steep for 10–15 minutes. Pour through a strainer into a cup and drink hot.

Note: 1–2 tablespoons of dried nettle herb can also be added to this tea to make it more nutritious for nursing mothers, or for anyone convalescing after an operation.

Above right: Red Clover, Hops, and Black Cohosh Tea
Right: Calendula flowers

Herbal Teas for Stress

Stress is a part of our daily life, and in most instances it is unavoidable. What can be improved is the way we deal with stress. The causes of stress can sometimes be insidious and hard to pinpoint. A constant, slowly building stress, such as an unfavorable workplace or an unhappy home situation, can bring you to a point where you can't remember when you last felt good. At other times, stress symptoms are obvious and straightforward. You can suddenly find yourself unable to cope, which can be a devastating situation.

Dealing with stress means recognizing first what the cause of the stress is, and then taking measures to address it. This can mean making lifestyle changes, dietary changes, perhaps even seeking counseling. Any positive change is worth it. Life is too short and beautiful to live it in an unhappy state of mind.

If you are stressed, take a good vitamin B-complex tablet with breakfast each day. Begin an exercise regime. It can be daily or every other day. Make sure it is something you enjoy: perhaps walking, swimming, dancing, cycling, jogging, or you might like going to the gym to do a workout.

The teas in this section help to alleviate many different types of stresses, such as those caused by grief, hormonal changes, sleepless nights, a desire to overachieve, moodiness, premenstrual tension, and low spirits. These teas will help you reap maximum benefit from any positive lifestyle changes you make, and they can help guide you onto a path of well-being.

Left: Chamomile and Lemongrass Tea

Rosemary, Skullcap, and Lavender Tea

After an unhappy event, it is normal to feel down. But if you find it hard to get on with life after some time has passed, this tea will help you let go of the blues. Rosemary is energizing, and it is an excellent stimulant that increases blood flow to the head, improves stamina, and aids concentration. Skullcap is often called the happy herb, and lavender is an effective and safe antidepressant.

Makes 2 cups (16 fl oz/500 ml)
serves 2–3

2 teaspoons chopped fresh rosemary leaves
2 teaspoons dried skullcap
2 teaspoons chopped fresh lavender flower/leaf
2 cups (16 fl oz/500 ml) boiling water

Combine the rosemary, skullcap, and lavender in a warmed ceramic or glass teapot. Add the boiling water, cover and let steep for 5–10 minutes. Strain, then drink.

Drink 3 cups of this tea each day for 1 to 2 weeks.

Chamomile and Lemon Balm Tea

This herbal tea is excellent for people who are perfectionists and find it hard to relax. If you become wound up as the day progresses and then can't unwind at the end of the day, this tea will become your best friend. I also suggest you omit caffeine from your diet.

Makes 1 cup (8 fl oz/250 ml)
serves 1

1 teaspoon dried chamomile flowers
1/2 teaspoon dried lemon balm leaves
1 cup (8 fl oz/250 ml) boiling water

Combine the chamomile and lemon balm in a warmed small ceramic or glass teapot. Add the boiling water, cover, and let steep for 5–10 minutes. Pour through a strainer into a cup and drink hot.

Drink 1 cup straight after work and then another just before bed for a restful, relaxed sleep.

Vervain and Valerian Tea

Headaches brought on by stress can be very debilitating. Those that develop after stressful situations are known as tension headaches. These occur because the muscles in the neck and shoulder tense up, restricting blood flow to the head. Vervain is a calming restorative and antispasmodic, making it good for migraines and headaches induced by nerves. Valerian has a distinct pungent smell and works well to reduce anxiety and tension. If you drink it when you know you might develop a tension headache, you could avoid one altogether.

Makes 1 cup (8 fl oz/250 ml)
serves 1

1/2 teaspoon dried vervain herb
1/2 teaspoon dried valerian root
1 cup (8 fl oz/250 ml) boiling water

Combine the vervain and valerian in a cup. Add the boiling water, cover, and let steep for 10 minutes. Strain, then drink hot.

Drink this tea as needed.

Caution: Avoid vervain when pregnant, as it is a uterine stimulant.

Chamomile and Lemongrass Tea

This tea should help those who have trouble sleeping. I also recommend that you remove caffeine from your diet, and avoid eating late or eating just before going to bed. Chamomile has a sedative effect without impairing any bodily functions. Lemongrass adds a pleasant citrus taste to the tea. Both are excellent digestive herbs.

Makes 1 cup (8 fl oz/250 ml)
serves 1

1 teaspoon dried chamomile flowers
1 teaspoon chopped dried lemongrass
1 cup (8 fl oz/250 ml) boiling water

Combine the chamomile and lemongrass in a wamed small ceramic or glass teapot or cup. Add the boiling water, cover, and let steep for 5–10 minutes. Strain, then drink hot.

Drink before going to bed each night.

Note: Four drops of white chestnut, a Bach flower remedy, can also be added to this tea. This can help to calm a mind that can't "switch off".

Oat Straw, Gotu Kola, and Passionflower Tea

Under stress, the nervous system tends to give up. If you have symptoms of anxiety, hyperventilation or palpitations, herbs and supplements can help to nurture and tone the nervous system. Oat straw is a restorative nerve herb (nervine), antidepressant, and nutritive, and contains calcium, silica, and vitamins B1, B2 and E. Gotu kola is also a nervine, and is calming to the body and mind. Passionflower is the flower of the passion fruit plant, and has a sedative effect without impairing alertness; it also has a relaxing effect on the body, inducing sleep.

Makes 2 cups (16 fl oz/500 ml)
serves 2–3

2 tablespoons dried oat straw
1 tablespoon dried gotu kola leaves
1 tablespoon dried passionflower
3 cups water (24 fl oz/750 ml)

Combine the oats, gotu kola, passionflower and water in a saucepan and bring to a boil. Reduce heat to medium-low, cover, and simmer until reduced by one-third. Strain and drink. Drink 1 cup of this tea 3 times a day for as long as needed.

Caution: Avoid oats straw if you are gluten sensitive or have coeliac disease. Alternatively, after decoction allow the liquid to settle then strain the clear herbal liquid.

Vitex and Oat Straw Tea

Sometimes a period can make you extremely sensitive. If you suffer low spirits, sensations of jealousy, suspicion, or behave neurotically before a period, you could be suffering from hormone imbalance. Vitex stabilizes imbalances, starting at the pituitary level, normalizing hormonal functions. Oat Straw also helps by nourishing the nervous system.

Makes 2 cups (16 fl oz/500 ml)
serves 2–3

1 tablespoon dried vitex berries
2 tablespoons dried oat straw
3 cups water (24 fl oz/750 ml)
honey to taste (optional)

Combine the vitex, oats straw, and water in a saucepan and bring to boil. Reduce heat to medium-low, cover, and simmer until reduced by one-third. Strain, then drink. Add honey to sweeten, if desired.

Drink 1 cup of this tea the first thing each morning for 3 months.

Caution: Avoid oats straw if you are gluten sensitive or have coeliac disease. Alternatively, after decoction allow the liquid to settle then strain the clear herbal liquid.

Right: Vitex and Oat Straw Tea

Meadowsweet, Lavender, and Dandelion Root Tea

Because of stress, you may find that you have lost your appetite and your tummy is in knots. To relax and aid your digestion, try this tea while preparing dinner. Meadowsweet is a digestive herb that relaxes and soothes the stomach. Lavender has an antistress, relaxing effect. Dandelion's mildly bitter taste encourages digestive juices to flow and enhances the appetite.

Makes 1 cup (8 fl oz/250 ml)
serves 1

1/2 teaspoon dried meadowsweet flowers and/or leaves
1/2 teaspoon dried or fresh lavender flowers and/or leaves
1/2 teaspoon dried dandelion root
1 cup (8 fl oz/250 ml) boiling water

Combine the meadowsweet, lavender, and dandelion in a warmed small ceramic or glass teapot or cup. Add the boiling water, cover, and let steep for 5–10 minutes. Strain and drink.

This tea is good to take before meals, and as an after-dinner digestive.

Rosemary and St. John's Wort Tea

This tea will help when you have lost interest in daily activities. Low spirits can creep up slowly, and sometimes we don't even realize it. St. John's wort has become popular recently for treating lowered activity and sadness. Rosemary is a brain stimulant that increases blood flow to the head. It also gives this tea a delightful spicy aroma.

Makes 1 cup (8 fl oz/250 ml)
serves 1

1 teaspoon chopped fresh rosemary leaves
1 teaspoon dried St. John's wort
1 cup (8 fl oz/250 ml) boiling water

Combine the rosemary and St. John's wort in a warmed small ceramic or glass teapot or cup. Add the boiling water, cover, and let steep for 5–10 minutes. Strain, then drink hot.

Drink 3 cups of this tea each day for 3–4 weeks. If low spirits do not go away, please visit your health care provider to resolve any underlying problem.

Caution: Avoid St. John's wort if you are taking blood thinning medication such as Warfarin.

Right: Rosemary and St. John's Wort Tea

Springtime Tonics

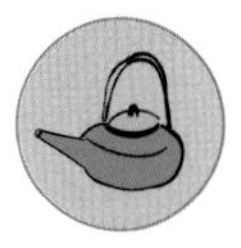

Springtime can be the busiest time of year for herbalists. Old and new patients come in seeking tonics to combat allergies. Today, more people than ever seem to be sensitive to allergens. Asthma sufferers are especially vulnerable to allergens, and they can develop eczema or hives as well as experiencing difficulty breathing.

Classic allergy signs are itchy eyes, sneezing, a blocked nose, a heavy feeling in the sinuses, and an extremely itchy throat. There are a number of things sufferers can do to alleviate the symptoms. They can take plenty of vitamin C to reduce inflammatory reactions to allergens. They should also take magnesium, zinc, and selenium to reduce viscosity (stickiness) in the lungs. Their diet should be free of preservatives, additives, and artificial flavorings. If they suffer from constipation, this should also be addressed. They also need to wash all new clothing, towels, and sheets before use to remove formaldehyde or any other chemical treatments.

Some people may need to explore breathing therapy, especially if they breathe mostly through the mouth. They should also avoid unfermented dairy foods, such as milk, ice creams, and processed cheeses, as these products can increase mucus production in the lungs, throat, and sinuses. Fried foods should be avoided, as well as refined carbohydrates, such as white bread, and refined sugar intake should be decreased.

Herbs can be used to treat allergies very well. They mostly relieve the symptoms, but they can provide great relief. Herbs are free of side effects and do not dry up the mucous membranes; instead, they heal and tonify them, clearing the sinuses and relieving congestion. Making lifestyle changes and drinking some of the following teas may be all you need to do to improve your allergies. These teas could help make life a breeze during beautiful spring days.

Elder and Eyebright Tea

This tea can help if you have watery, itchy, red, and very irritated eyes, and it can also help with conjunctivitis. Elder has numerous therapeutic qualities, including reducing mucus production. In the past, elder water was thought to remove freckles and whiten the skin. Elder leaves made into a poultice can be used to ease bruising and injury. The combination of eyebright and elder makes the perfect cold and influenza remedy, as eyebright acts as a tonic for the mucous membranes.

Makes 1 cup (8 fl oz/250 ml)
serves 1

1 teaspoon dried elder flowers and/or leaves
1 teaspoon dried eyebright herb
1 cup (8 fl oz/250 ml) boiling water

Combine the elder and eyebright in a warmed small ceramic or glass teapot or cup. Add the boiling water, cover, and let steep for 5 minutes. Strain, then drink hot.

Drink 3 cups of this tea hot every day to encourage sweating and to help clear a cold. It can also be cooled and used as an eyewash.

Ribwort and Eyebright Tea

Sinus sufferers feel pressure behind their eyes. This is due to congestion in the sinus cavities, which may cause headaches, a blocked nose, and dark circles under the eyes. Sinus sufferers should check with their dentist to ensure their sinus troubles are not caused by an abscessed tooth. This can lead to infection in the bone, which can be quite serious. Ribwort (plantain) is an effective decongestant that tones the mucous membranes, breaks down mucus, and clears the sinuses. Eyebright, like ribwort, is a decongestant, and has the added advantage of being an anti-inflammatory that soothes gritty, itchy eyes.

Makes 1 cup (8 fl oz/250 ml)
serves 1

1 teaspoon dried ribwort (plantain) leaves
1 teaspoon dried eyebright herb
1 cup (8 fl oz/250 ml) boiling water

Combine the ribwort and eyebright in a cup. Add the boiling water, cover, and let steep for 5–10 minutes. Strain, then drink hot.

Drink 3 to 4 cups of this tea a day for 3 to 7 days, until symptoms are relieved.

Note: If an infection is present, add 1 teaspoon dried echinacea to this mix.

Chickweed, Calendula, and Nettle Tea

Eczema, hives, and other forms of dermatitis can appear as red, itchy rashes. Chickweed is a cooling herb, and it can soothe any angry red rash. The bright yellow-gold calendula flower is healing, anti-inflammatory, and a strong antifungal. Nettle has astringent qualities. In ancient Rome, Caesar's troops used to beat themselves with nettle to rid themselves of arthritis, aches, and pains.

Makes 2 cups (16 fl oz/500 ml)
serves 2–3

2 tablespoons chopped fresh chickweed herb
2 tablespoons chopped fresh calendula flowers
1 tablespoon dried nettle herb
2 cups (16 fl oz/500 ml) boiling water

Combine the chickweed, calendula, and nettle in a warmed ceramic or glass teapot. Add the boiling water, cover, and let steep for 10 minutes. Strain, then drink hot.

Drink 3 cups of this tea a day. You can also use a clean cloth to sponge the strained tea onto affected areas to soothe them. Chickweed tea can be added to a bath to further soothe the skin.

Echinacea, Dandelion, and Licorice Tea

If you wake up with a succession of sneezes and an unbearably itchy nose every morning during spring, try this tea. Both echinacea and licorice are antiallergic herbs, while dandelion acts as a desensitizer, strengthening the liver. Echinacea is native to America. It has long been used by Native Americans for its strong antimicrobial effect, and has now become well known all over the world.

Makes 2 cups (16 fl oz/500 ml)
serves 2–3

1 tablespoon dried echinacea root
1 tablespoon dried dandelion root
2 teaspoons ground licorice root
2 cups (16 fl oz/500 ml) boiling water

Combine the echinacea, dandelion, and licorice in a saucepan. Add the boiling water, cover, then simmer over medium-low heat until reduced by one-third, about 15 minutes. Strain, then drink hot.

Drink 1 cup of this tea a day prior to and during spring.

Caution: Avoid licorice if you suffer from high blood pressure.

Licorice Tea

Licorice is available as a chopped root or in ground form. This tea may help to minimize the severity of asthma attacks if it is drunk regularly. It is also useful if you suffer bronchial tightness in the chest. Licorice helps to break down catarrh in the respiratory system, has a pleasant flavor, and helps to prevent allergies.

Makes 2 cups (16 fl oz/500 ml)
serves 2–3

1 tablespoon dried licorice root
2 cups (16 fl oz/500 ml) boiling water

Put the licorice in a warmed ceramic or glass teapot. Add the boiling water, cover and let steep for 10 minutes. Strain and drink.

Drink 3 cups of this tea a day if you have excess phlegm in your respiratory system.

Caution: Avoid licorice if you have high blood pressure.

Echinacea and Thyme Tea

Allergens can cause bronchial constriction. Echinacea is antiviral, antifungal, and antibacterial. It helps to build up the body's resistance to allergies. To gain the full benefit of echinacea, it needs to be decocted. Thyme is particularly good for clearing the lungs. Thyme is antimicrobial and can be refreshing for the whole body. A face cloth dipped into this hot tea and then applied directly onto the chest is very effective for chest congestion.

Makes 2 cups (16 fl oz/500 ml)
serves 2–3

1 tablespoon dried echinacea herb
1 tablespoon dried thyme leaves and/or flowers
3 cups (24 fl oz/750 ml) water

Combine the echinacea, thyme and water in a saucepan, cover, and bring to a boil. Reduce heat to medium-low and simmer, covered, for 15 minutes, or until reduced by one-third. Strain, then drink hot.

Drink 2 cups of this tea every day for several days.

Caution: Avoid thyme during pregnancy, as it is a uterine stimulant.

***Right:** Echinacea and Thyme Tea*

Herbal Teas for Cleansing

Cleansing, or detoxifying, is all about improving the digestive system—your liver, kidneys, and bowel function—to provide an overall feeling of well-being. Years of dietary and lifestyle neglect can lead to sluggish digestion and bowels. This in turn can cause skin outbreaks, headaches, vagueness, loss of concentration, fatigue, and an overall sensation of feeling under par.

Many of my clients suffer from reflux, or heartburn, and other symptoms that go with indigestion: wind, burping, discomfort after meals, and so on. It is common for many people to live with this conditions for years, thinking it is normal. It is not, and in most cases it is due to low stomach acid and low digestive juices. There are a number of ways to combat this condition.

Many of us tend to forget how important drinking water can be. When thirst hits us we often reach for a coffee, soft drink, or cordial, all of which tax the kidneys. Coffee is a diuretic and can dehydrate the body—notice how dry your mouth tastes after the next coffee you have. The sugar in soft drinks and cordials are often too heavy for the kidneys to deal with effectively. A glass of warm, filtered water first thing every morning gives the kidneys a thorough flush. (Drink room-temperature water during summer.). Cleansing the kidneys in this simple and gentle way will give your body a great start to the day, every day. Add a squeeze of fresh lemon or lime for flavor, and carry a bottle with you wherever you go.

To aid your digestion, mix 1 tablespoon apple cider vinegar or the juice from a lemon quarter into a glass of warm water. Drink this before each meal. You should also eat bitter salads and bitter foods, such as green olives, with your main meal to increase the secretion of digestive enzymes. Little additions like these can make all the difference.

Yarrow, Dandelion, and Alfalfa Tea

Some women accumulate a few pounds of fluid just before their period. Their urine output is less, and their fingers can swell. Yarrow is a tonic for the blood vessels and acts as a gentle diuretic. Dandelion leaf is a kidney tonic that nourishes and cleanses the body by flushing the urinary system. Alfalfa is high in iron.

Makes 1 cup (8 fl oz/250 ml)
serves 1

2 teaspoons chopped fresh yarrow flowers and/or leaves
2 teaspoons chopped fresh dandelion leaves
1 teaspoon alfalfa seeds
1 cup (8 fl oz/250 ml) boiling water

Combine the yarrow, dandelion, and alfalfa in a warmed small ceramic or glass teapot or cup. Add the boiling water, cover, and let steep for 10–15 minutes. Strain and drink.

Drink 3 cups of the tea each day around period time.

Note: The slightly bitter taste of yarrow will override the other flavors in this tea. You can add some chopped lavender flowers, if desired, to make the tea more fragrant. Lavender may also help with premenstrual tension.

Corn Silk, Buchu, Uva Ursi, and Peppermint Tea

Frequent urination, burning, and inability to completely empty your bladder are all symptoms of urinary tract infection. Cystitis, otherwise known as the honeymoon disease, is common. Most women suffering with cystitis have had several courses of antibiotics, but the infection just keeps coming back. Herbs can help clear the infection out of your system once and for all.

Makes 3 cups (24 fl oz/750 ml)
serves 3–4

4 tablespoons chopped dried corn silk
2 tablespoons chopped dried buchu leaves
2 tablespoons dried uva ursi leaves
1 tablespoon dried peppermint leaves
3 cups (24 fl oz/750 ml) boiling water

Combine the corn silk, buchu, uva ursi and peppermint in a warmed ceramic or glass teapot. Add the boiling water, cover, and let steep for 10 minutes. Pour through a strainer and drink.

Drink 3 cups of this tea each day for 1–2 weeks.

Note: Uva ursi may cause cramping in some people. In addition to this tea, drink at least 8–12 cups (2–3 L) of filtered water daily to help flush the infection out of your system.

Ginger and Peppermint Tea

This tea works well for all forms of nausea, such as those caused by food poisoning, excessive alcohol intake, and travel sickness. It is also great when you are pregnant, and is very safe. Ginger is settling to the stomach and can be used on its own if the need arises. Peppermint is refreshing and cleansing to the mouth, and is an effective antispasmodic. Peppermint can also be used on its own to treat morning sickness and other forms of nausea.

Makes 1 cup (8 fl oz/250 ml)
serves 1

1 teaspoon peeled and grated fresh ginger
1/2 teaspoon dried peppermint leaves
1 cup (8 fl oz/250 ml) boiling water

Combine the ginger and peppermint in a warmed small ceramic or glass teapot or cup. Add the boiling water, cover, and let steep for 5–10 minutes. Strain, then drink hot.

Drink this tea whenever you feel nauseous or as a preventative before traveling.

Peppermint and Yarrow Tea

One of the best ways to avoid indigestion is to eat sensibly. Start your meal with a bitter food, such as an arugula (rocket) salad, to get your digestive enzymes flowing. And never, ever overeat—frequent small meals throughout the day work best. This tea helps when you have indigestion, as the bitter taste of yarrow encourages digestion, and peppermint has a soothing, antinausea effect that eases the heavy sensation in the stomach.

Makes 1 cup (8 fl oz/250 ml)
serves 1

2 teaspoons chopped fresh yarrow leaves and/or flowers
1 teaspoon dried peppermint leaves
1 cup (8 fl oz/250 ml) boiling water

Combine the peppermint and yarrow in a warmed small ceramic or glass teapot or cup. Add the boiling water, cover, and let steep for 5–10 minutes. Strain, then drink hot.

Drink 1 cup of this tea after a heavy meal or when you suffer with indigestion.

Dandelion Tea

The young, jagged, toothlike leaves of the dandelion plant make a delicious bitter addition to salads and are great as a kidney tonic in tea. Dandelion leaf is one of the strongest diuretics, and it is rich in potassium. Dandelion root tastes bitter. It is used to treat liver conditions, and to help with constipation and jaundice.

Makes 1 cup (8 fl oz/250 ml)
serves 1

2 teaspoons dried dandelion root, or 1 tablespoon chopped fresh dandelion leaf
1 cup (8 fl oz/250 ml) water

Combine the dandelion root or leaf in a glass and add the water. Cover and let soak overnight. Strain and drink.

Drink 1 to 2 cups of this tea daily.

Dandelion, Licorice, and Ginger Tea

Binge drinking is harmful to the body. If you know you are going to drink a lot of alcohol, make sure you take a vitamin B-complex tablet and 3,000 mg vitamin C pre- and post-drinking, with some food. One of the best preventatives of alcohol dehydration is drinking an equal amount of water with alcohol during the evening. This tea can help after a big night out. The bitter dandelion root will rejuvenate the liver, while the sweet-tasting licorice acts as an adaptogen for the adrenals, cleansing and nourishing the system. Ginger can settle that seedy feeling in the stomach.

Makes 2 cups (16 fl oz/500 ml)
serves 2–3

1 teaspoon dried dandelion root
1/2 teaspoon ground licorice root
1/2 teaspoon peeled and grated fresh ginger
2 cups (16 fl oz/500 ml) boiling water

Combine the dandelion, licorice and ginger in a warmed ceramic or glass teapot. Add the boiling water, cover, and let steep for 10 minutes. Pour through a strainer into a warmed cup and drink.

Drink 1 to 2 cups of this tea on rising and then 1 cup each day for 1 week to help the body regain strength.

Right: Dandelion Tea

Chamomile and Aniseed Tea

This tea is gentle, safe, and delicious to drink. It can quickly soothe and quiet a frantic, colicky baby, but be sure to boil the water for 10 minutes when preparing a bottle for a baby, to ensure that you kill all the bacteria. Chamomile is antispasmodic and a relaxant. Aniseed adds a menthol-like taste to the tea and acts as a carminative by helping to reduce flatulence and cramping.

Makes 1/2 cup (4 fl oz/125 ml)
serves 1

1 teaspoon dried chamomile flowers
1/2 teaspoon aniseed, slightly crushed
1/2 cup (4 fl oz/125 ml) boiling water

Combine the chamomile and aniseed in a warmed small ceramic or glass teapot or cup. Add the boiling water, cover, and let steep for 5–10 minutes. Allow to cool to lukewarm for babies. Strain, then drink.

Caution: Honey can be added to sweeten, but do not add when preparing for babies under 2 years of age.

Nettle and Clivers Tea

This tea is nourishing and cleansing for the lymphatic system. Nettle is rich in iron and vitamin C and is supportive for the whole body. It is a great treatment for gout, allergic reactions such as hives and eczema, and for debility. Clivers is one of the best lymphatic herbs for those who suffer recurrent sore throats or persistent swollen glands, especially after glandular fever. It clears congested lymph nodes.

Makes 2 cups (16 fl oz/500 ml)
serves 2–3

2–3 tablespoons dried nettle herb
2–3 tablespoons dried clivers
2 cups (16 fl oz/500 ml) boiling water

Combine the nettle and clivers in a warmed ceramic or glass teapot. Add the boiling water, cover, and let steep for 10–15 minutes. Strain, then drink.

Drink up to 3 cups of this tea each day.

Right: Chamomile and Aniseed Tea

Herbal Teas for Immunity

Have you noticed how often people catch a cold or the flu these days? Getting sick once in a while is normal. Naturopathically, catching a cold every few years is thought of as a good cleansing. Children get sick more often than adults, as they still need to build up resistance and strengthen their immune system. But it is thought that the heavy use of antibiotics in our society has worked against us. Many strains of microbes have become resistant to antibiotics. They have mutated (changed their form), and the antibiotics don't work as well they used to, if at all, against them. And our bodies are less resistant to these microbes, causing more illnesses.

Instead of becoming reliant on antibiotics to cure our ills, we should look for ways to prevent these common diseases. The best way to do this is to eat well-balanced, wholesome meals that are pesticide and additive free, and made with fresh ingredients. We should also make our homes and workplaces more safe by using fewer sprays, chemical cleaners, and insect repellents.

Zinc is responsible for many functions in the body; one of them is immunity. If the body is low in zinc, it can be susceptible to colds, coughs, and recurrent sore throats. Foods that are rich in zinc include oysters, seafood, pumpkin seeds (pepitas), and sunflower seeds.

The following teas are useful as preventatives and for halting an infection in its track. They include some that will soothe sore and scratchy throats, ease a cough, expel mucus, and help you sweat an illness out and make a full recovery. Keep in mind that teas are not as strong as a liquid extract that an herbalist might prescribe. If symptoms do not go away, visit your health care provider for a thorough assessment.

Licorice, Ginger, and Yarrow Tea

This delicious tea will create an inner warmth to help you survive cold, gloomy winter days. It is a good all-round tonic. Licorice is particularly helpful for treating upper and lower respiratory conditions and is used extensively in Chinese and Western herbal medicine. Ginger is warming and soothing to the chest and stomach. Yarrow, like ginger, acts as a diaphoretic (brings on a sweat), and is a decongestant with strong antiallergenic properties.

Makes 1 cup (8 fl oz/250 ml)
serves 1

1 tablespoon chopped fresh yarrow leaves and/or flowers
1/2 teaspoon ground licorice root
1/2 teaspoon peeled and grated fresh ginger
1 cup (8 fl oz/250 ml) boiling water

Combine the yarrow, licorice and ginger in a warmed small ceramic or glass teapot or cup. Add the boiling water, cover, and let steep for 3–5 minutes. Strain and drink.

Drink 1 cup of this tea each day approaching, and during, winter.

Cautions: Licorice should be avoided if you have high blood pressure. Yarrow should be avoided during pregnancy.

Licorice and Ginger Tea

If you feel a cold coming on, drink this tea quick! It will help to expel heat from your body, bringing on a good sweat to help your body fight the infection and cool down. Licorice is a sweet and pleasant-tasting herb. Ginger is hot and warming; the quantity might need to be adjusted to suit your taste buds. The more ginger you use the better its effect.

Makes about 3 cups (24 fl oz/750 ml)
serves 4–5

2 tablespoons ground licorice root
2 tablespoons peeled and grated fresh ginger
3 cups (24 fl oz/750 ml) boiling water

Combine the licorice and ginger in a warmed ceramic or glass teapot. Add the boiling water, cover, and let steep for 5–10 minutes. Strain, then drink piping hot.

It's important to drink this tea while it's hot, to encourage your body to sweat—this will help your body to fight the virus. Aim to drink 1 cup every 1 to 2 hours on the first day, then gradually taper off to 2 to 4 cups a day for up to 4 days, or until symptoms subside.

Caution: Avoid licorice if you have high blood pressure.

Goldenrod, Eyebright, and Ribwort Tea

This tea is for both children and adults. Goldenrod, eyebright, and ribwort (plaintain) are decongestants, tonics to the mucous membranes. For this reason, this tea is good for those who have an intolerance to dairy products. Eyebright is the first thing I think of for mucous membrane conditions. Goldenrod is antiseptic and anti-inflammatory. Ribwort is also anti-inflammatory, grows everywhere as a weed, and can be plucked out of the garden or used dry.

Makes 2 cups (16 fl oz/500 ml)
serves 2–3

1 teaspoon dried goldenrod herb
2 teaspoons dried eyebright herb
2 teaspoons dried ribwort (plantain) leaves
2 cups (16 fl oz/500 ml) boiling water

Combine the goldenrod, eyebright, and ribwort in a warmed ceramic or glass teapot. Add the boiling water, cover, and let steep for 10 minutes.

Drink 3 cups of this tea a day for a week or so.

Note: This tea can be varied by using only two of the herbs, if desired, or by adding 1 teaspoon of ground licorice root for its added effect and taste.

Caution: Avoid licorice if you have high blood pressure.

Horehound, Mullein, and Thyme Tea

A buildup of mucus in the throat and lungs can linger if not cleared promptly and effectively. Horehound has a gentle, stimulating, expectorant action on the lungs, which encourages the clearance of phlegm. This makes it good for treating bronchitis and asthma. Mullein soothes itchy and irritating coughs. Thyme is a strong antimicrobial, antispasmodic, and relaxant for the bronchi. Thyme tea on its own makes a great gargle for gum disease and sore throats.

Makes 2 cups (16 fl oz/500 ml)
serves 2–3

2 teaspoons dried horehound flowers and/or leaves
2 teaspoons dried mullein flowers and/or leaves
2 teaspoons dried thyme herb
2 cups (16 fl oz/500 ml) boiling water

Combine the horehound, mullein, and thyme in a warmed ceramic or glass teapot. Add the boiling water, cover, and let steep for 10 minutes. Strain, then drink hot.

Drink 2–3 cups a day of this tea while it is quite hot, for 5–6 days, or until your chest has cleared.

Caution: Avoid thyme during pregnancy, as it is a uterine stimulant.

Sage and Astragalus Tea

This tea is recommended for those who suffer recurrent sore throats and swollen glands. It does wonders after a bout of glandular fever, as it cleanses and clears congestion in the lymphatic system. Bacteria that thrive in an inflamed throat love sugar, because it gives them food so they can multiply, so you should also avoid all foods containing sugar and refined carbohydrates. Sage is strong in taste, antimicrobial, and makes an excellent gargle on its own. Astragalus is a sweet and warming immunostimulant herb that encourages healing and tissue regeneration.

Makes 1 cup (8 fl oz/250 ml)
serves 1

2 teaspoons crumbled dried sage leaves, or
1 tablespoon chopped fresh sage
1 teaspoon dried astragalus root
1 cup (8 fl oz/250 ml) boiling water

Combine the sage and astragalus in a warmed small ceramic or glass teapot or cup. Add the boiling water and let steep for 5 minutes. Strain and drink.

Drink 1 cup of this tea twice a day for 1 week.

Caution: Sage should be avoided if you have epilepsy.

Licorice and Echinacea Tea

A healthy liver plays an important role in managing allergies, as it helps to minimize reactions. Being aware of what you put in your body, and what you expose it to, can and will make all the difference. Licorice and echinacea both strengthen the body's defenses and help it to be less reactive to allergens. Licorice is a tonic for the liver and encourages regular bowel motions so that constipation is avoided. Echinacea is an effective immunostimulant and antimicrobial, with the fresh plant being more potent than the dried.

Makes 2 cups (16 fl oz/500 ml)
serves 2–3

1 tablespoon dried licorice root
2 tablespoons chopped fresh echinacea flowers/roots or
1 tablespoon dried echinacea root
3 cups (16 fl oz/500 ml) boiling water

Combine the licorice, echinacea, and water in a medium saucepan. Bring to a boil over high heat. Reduce heat to medium-low, cover, then simmer for 15 minutes, or until reduced by one-third. Strain, then drink hot.

Drink 1 to 2 cups of this tea a day as a preventative, or 3 cups a day during illness.

Caution: Licorice should be avoided if you have high blood pressure.

Right: Sage and Astragalus Tea

Thyme, Elecampane, and Cardamom Tea

This tea is great for persistent wet coughs, as it encourages the removal of mucus built up in the lungs. Thyme makes an excellent expectorant and antispasmodic, at the same time relaxing bronchial constriction in the lungs. The fragrant volatile oil of thyme is a good antiseptic and antimicrobial. Elecampane facilitates the removal of mucus from the lungs by stimulating and inducing coughing. Cardamom is warming to the body and adds flavor.

Makes 1 cup (8 fl oz/250 ml)
serves 1

1 teaspoon shredded dried elecampane root
1 cup (8 fl oz/250 ml) water
1 teaspoon dried thyme leaves and/or flowers
pinch of ground cardamom

Soak the elecampane in the water overnight. Strain and then heat the liquid in a small saucepan until almost boiling. Add the thyme, remove from heat, cover, and let steep for 5–10 minutes. Pour through a strainer into a cup, stir in the cardamom, and drink hot.

Drink up to 3 cups a day.

Note: If you find that drinking this tea stimulates too much coughing, replace elecampane with marshmallow root, which is soothing and relaxes irritating coughs.

Oat Straw and Alfalfa Tea

This tea is ideal if you have been sick for some time, have little appetite, and don't feel quite yourself. It can be taken any time you are feeling rundown. Oat straw has a bland taste, but it strengthens the nervous system and is rich in silica and calcium. Alfalfa is rich in iron, vitamin A, B, C, D, and E, and is particularly good for convalescence.

Makes 2 cups (16 fl oz/500 ml)
serves 2–3

3 tablespoons dried oat straw
1 tablespoon alfalfa seed
2 cups (16 fl oz/500 ml) water

Combine the oat straw, alfalfa seed, and water in a small saucepan. Bring to a boil over high heat. Reduce heat to medium-low, cover, and then simmer for 20 minutes, or until reduced by one-third. Strain, then drink.

Drink 1 cup of this tea every 3 hours for 2–4 weeks.

Note: You can add 1/2 teaspoon of ground licorice root to give this tea extra benefits for the adrenal glands, and to improve its taste.

Caution: Licorice should be avoided if you have high blood pressure. Avoid oat straw if you are sensitive to gluten or have coeliac disease.

Right: Oat Straw and Alfalfa Tea

Fruit Tea Blends

Tea shops shelves are filled with colorful canisters with wonderful surprises inside them. I was invited to take a look inside one of the canisters, and as it was opened I was engulfed by the magical aroma of dried strawberries. I don't think I'll ever forget that fragrance. And that's one of the delightful pleasures of making a fruit tea: the aroma is unforgettable.

Fruit teas are made from the fruits of various trees, plants, and shrubs. Fruits such as berries, rosehips (the ripe fruit of the rose), and citrus are the varieties most often used. They can be used medicinally, depending on the variety, or enjoyed just for their tangy flavor.

In Chinese medicine, the sweet taste of fruit is associated with weight gain and the stomach. Fruits are considered yin, with cold and damp. The orange, for example, native to China before it spread to Arabia and the rest of the Mediterranean, is used in Chinese medicine as a digestive stimulant and to improve qi (the flow of energy), as well as a treatment for phlegm, coughs, and insomnia.

Sacred hawthorn berries, with their slightly sweet flavor, were known as mother of the heart because they work on the cardiac actions within the body. They can relax the heart and arteries, decreasing blood pressure. Hawthorn berries were added to bread in England during World War I to bring down the blood pressure of the population.

Fruits are usually high in vitamin C and bioflavonoids, which make them great antioxidants. Berries, with their deep purple colors, are great for the eyes; they improve eyesight, relieve tired, red eyes, and constrict the blood vessels in the eye, making them look clear and vibrant. Drinking a good strong cup of berry tea once or twice daily will work wonders.

To make your own fruit tea, the fruit needs to be dried. Pick or select your fruit when it is just ripe. Slice the fruit, then spread it evenly out on a drying surface and remember to turn it over often to prevent mold from forming on it. (See page 103 for more details on drying fruit.)

Bilberry and Green Tea

Bilberry and green tea are both very strong antioxidants. Bilberry has long been used therapeutically for glaucoma and other eye-related diseases. Bilberry is diuretic and astringent, and has a cooling and drying effect on the body. It also improves the production of insulin, which is useful in the treatment of adult onset diabetes. The flavor of green tea is masked by the flavor of the bilberry; however, its digestive-enhancing qualities are still present.

Makes 1 cup (8 fl oz/250 ml)
serves 1

1 teaspoon dried bilberries
1/2 teaspoon green tea leaves
1 cup (8 fl oz/250 ml) boiling water

Combine the bilberry and green tea leaves in a warmed small ceramic or glass teapot or cup. Add the boiling water, cover, and let steep for 5–10 minutes. Strain, then drink hot to warm.

Hawthorn Berry, Lemon Rind and Lime Blossom Tea

This tea has a slight sweet-to-sour taste that warms the body. Tests in Japan show that hawthorn berries have positive cardiac effects, reducing blood pressure and the heart rate. It is also useful in the treatment of edema and dyspnea (shortness of breath). Lemon rind contains citrus flavonoids that improve varicose veins and are antihistaminic. Lime blossoms also have cardiac properties, reducing blood pressure and helping nervous disorders.

Makes 2 cups (16 fl oz/500 ml)
serves 2–3

1 tablespoon dried hawthorn berries
1/2 teaspoon grated lemon zest (rind)
1 tablespoon dried lime blossom
2 cups (16 fl oz/500 ml) boiling water

Place the hawthorn berries, lemon zest and lime blossom in a warmed ceramic or glass teapot. Add the boiling water and let steep for 10–15 minutes. Strain, then drink hot or cool.

Drink one to two cups of the tea each day.

Orange, Cinnamon, and Peach Tea

Orange and orange zest have been used to flavor food and drinks for decades. Orange is used as a stomachic (calming and relaxing to the digestive system). The flavonoids in orange are also anti-inflammatory, antibacterial, and antifungal. Cinnamon is a gentle circulatory stimulant, as it increases blood flow, thus warming the hands and feet. It has been used for thousands of years to treat nausea and vomiting, and it is also a digestive healing herb. Peach adds a delightful color and flavor to this aromatic brew. If dried peaches are not available, substitute dried apricots.

Makes 2 cups (16 fl oz/500 ml)
serves 2–3

1 teaspoon grated fresh orange zest (rind)
1 teaspoon ground cinnamon
1 tablespoon chopped dried peach
2 cups (16 fl oz/500 ml) boiling water

Combine the orange zest, cinnamon, and peach in a warmed ceramic or glass teapot. Add the boiling water, cover, and let steep for 5 minutes.

Note: You can strain this tea to drink as a refresher during summer or as a digestive after a heavy meal.

Juniper and Cranberry Juice Tea

Juniper, with its pungent, bittersweet flavor, has long been used as an antiseptic that flushes and cleanses the entire urinary system. It is useful in treating cystitis, gout, and other types of rheumatism. Cranberry has a long history of soothing and healing urinary mucus. It makes acid urine less acidic, thus decreasing the burning pain associated with cystitis.

Makes 2 cups (16 fl oz/500 ml)
serves 2–3

2 teaspoons dried juniper berries
1 cup (8 fl oz/250 ml) boiling water
1 cup (8 fl oz/250 ml) cranberry juice

Put the juniper berries in a warmed ceramic or glass teapot. Add the boiling water, cover, and let steep for 10 minutes. Allow to cool and then combine with the cranberry juice.

Drink 1 cup twice daily.

Caution: Women who are pregnant should avoid juniper, as it is a uterine stimulant. Anyone suffering kidney disease should also avoid juniper.

Lemon, Aniseed, and Fennel Seed Tea

Lemon juice and its zest are natural antimicrobials. Aniseed drinks were once a popular remedy for colds and flu. Both aniseed and fennel are lung-cleansing tonics, and they are given to women after delivery to encourage milk flow and to reduce colic in babies. Both have a slight licorice flavor. Fennel seeds have a reputation for suppressing the appetite if chewed before meals, and they also make an excellent breath freshener.

Makes 2 cups (16 fl oz/500 ml)
serves 2–3

1–2 teaspoons grated lemon zest (rind)
1 teaspoon aniseed
1–2 teaspoons fennel seeds
2 cups (16 fl oz/500 ml) boiling water

Combine the lemon zest, aniseed, and fennel seeds in a warmed ceramic or glass teapot. Add the boiling water, cover, and let steep for 10 minutes. Strain, then drink hot.

Drink 2–3 cups of this tea each day.

Lemon and Mint Tea

Lemon and mint tea is appropriate during the winter months as a warming tonic on a cold day. The lemon soothes sore throats and helps relieve colds. The rich vitamin C content in lemon helps combat colds and flu, while warming the body when drunk hot. Lemon and mint are both digestives, and can be taken after a heavy meal to aid digestion.

Makes 1 cup (8fl oz/250ml)
serves 1

1 teaspoon dried peppermint leaf
1 cup (8 fl oz/250 ml) boiling water
2 teaspoons lemon juice
honey to taste

Put the dried peppermint leaves in a warmed small ceramic or glass teapot or cup. Add the boiling water, cover, and let steep for 5 minutes. Strain, then add the lemon juice and honey.

Drink 2–3 cups a day for a week if you have a cold or a sore throat. Drink 1 cup after a heavy meal to relieve indigestion.

Black Currant and Cardamom Tea

Black currant is widely used to flavor food and as an ingredient in cereals and mixed dried nuts. High in vitamin C, the purplish-black fruits are used to treat diarrhea due to their high tannin content. Cardamom, native to India and Sri Lanka, is widely used as a culinary spice in foods such as curries, and it is commonly used to flavor Turkish coffee. It has antispasmodic activity, is calming to the digestive system, and is stimulating to the body.

Makes 1 cup (8 fl oz/250 ml)
serves 2–3

1 teaspoon dried black currants
1/4 teaspoon ground cardamom
1 cup (8 fl oz/250 ml) boiling water

Combine the black currants and cardamom in a warmed ceramic or glass teapot. Add the boiling water, cover, and let steep for 5 minutes. Strain, then drink hot.

Drink 1–2 cups a day, as required.

Right: Black Currant and Cardamom Tea

Dried Strawberry and Apple Tea

This tea can be drunk simply for pleasure as the taste and aroma are lovely. Strawberry is also mildly astringent, and is a diuretic. Both strawberries and apples are high in vitamin C.

Makes 1 cup (8 fl oz/250 ml)
serves 1

1 teaspoon chopped dried strawberry
1 teaspoon chopped dried apple
1 cup (8 fl oz/250 ml) boiling water

Combine the strawberry and apple in a warmed small ceramic or glass teapot or cup. Add the boiling water, cover, and let steep for 10 minutes. Drink hot, straining it first, if you like.

Hibiscus and Elderberry Tea

These two fruits are packed with vitamin C and anti-microbial properties. It is used medicinally to treat coughs, fever, and painful menstruation. Elderberry has long been used in England in making pies, preserves, and syrups. It is a decongestant and a tonic to the mucous membranes.

Makes 2 cups (16 fl oz/500 ml)
serves 2–3

1 tablespoon dried hibiscus calyces
1 tablespoon fresh or 2 teaspoons dried elderberries
2 cups (16 fl oz/500 ml) boiling water

Combine the hibiscus and elderberries in a warmed ceramic or glass teapot. Add the boiling water, cover, and let steep for 10 minutes. Strain, then drink hot.

Raspberry and Hibiscus Tea

The leaves of the raspberry plant have long been used to treat women, especially during pregnancy. It is used to relieve morning sickness and prepare the uterus for birth, as well as for tonifying and strengthening the cervix. Its astringent taste is due to tannins. The tannin content in raspberry relieves diarrhea, and makes raspberry tea a good gargle for mouth and throat infections. Hibiscus, with its citrus taste and bright red color, makes this a beautiful and flavorful tea.

Makes 1 cup (8 fl oz/250 ml)
serves 1

1 teaspoon dried raspberry leaves and/or berries
1/2 teaspoon dried hibiscus calyces
1 cup (8 fl oz/250 ml) boiling water

Combine the raspberry and hibiscus in a warmed small ceramic or glass teapot or cup. Add the boiling water, cover, and let steep for 10 minutes. Strain, then drink hot.

Drink up to 2 cups a day for the last 3 months before the birth of a baby to prepare for an easy delivery, and drink during labor to assist the birth.

Vitex and Bilberry Tea

The plant *Vitex agnus-castus* has a pretty whirl of purple flowers and produces a lifesaving fruit that many women swear by for relieving premenstrual tension. Vitex will also increase lactation for nursing mothers. It is best taken first thing in the morning, as it works by regulating the pituitary gland. (If you suffer from PMS, you should also remove all caffeine-containing foods from your diet, as caffeine increases tension, worry, and anxiety.) Bilberry strengthens small blood vessels and is rich in bioflavonoids (antioxidants). This deep-purple tea is pretty when brewed in a glass teapot.

Makes 2 cups (16 fl oz/500 ml)
serves 2–3

1 tablespoon chopped dried vitex berries
2 teaspoons chopped dried bilberries
2 cups (16 fl oz/500 ml) boiling water

Combine the vitex and bilberries in a warmed small ceramic or glass teapot. Add the boiling water, cover, and let steep for 5–10 minutes. Strain, then drink hot.

Drink up to 2 cups a day.

EXOTIC FLORAL BLENDS

Floral teas are ideal to brew in a glass teapot. The colour of the petals will surprise your guests and so will the flavors of the flowers.

Flowers add serenity and peace to homes and workplaces, and can bring a smile to the face in seconds. Both because of their beauty and their fragility, they have been given as tokens of love and as offerings of worship to the gods throughout human history.

Flowers are highly regarded medicinally, and are used extensively to treat a variety of ailments, both in Chinese and Western herbalism. When dried correctly, flowers should retain their original color—discard if they do not. Chinese herbalists granulate some of their floral teas in a freeze-drying process. Sweetened chrysanthemum granules, for example, can be bought freeze-dried in little sachets, and they make a very refreshing tea that helps to soothe and nourish the eyes.

Left: Chrysanthemum and Ginger Tea

Chrysanthemum and Ginger Tea

Chrysanthemum is both sweet and bitter, and has a slightly cooling effect on the body. As a result, it is wonderful to drink on its own on hot, stuffy days. Mixed with ginger, however, the effect is counterbalanced, as ginger warms the body. Chrysanthemum tea can be well tolerated during fevers and headaches, it improves eyesight and can lower blood pressure. The yellow daisy-like flowers are used extensively in China as a poultice for sore, red eyes. Ginger adds a spicy flavor and assists fever treatment. It also flushes toxins caused by arthritis, and decreases pain and inflammation.

Makes 2 cups (16 fl oz/500 ml)
serves 2–3

1 tablespoon dried chrysanthemum flowers
1–2 teaspoons peeled and grated fresh ginger
2 cups (16 fl oz/500 ml) boiling water

Combine the chrysanthemum and ginger in a warmed ceramic or glass teapot. Add the boiling water, cover, and let steep for 10 minutes. Strain into a cup and drink hot.

Drink 1 cup of this tea every hour for fever, headaches, and arthritic pain.

Honeysuckle and Chamomile Tea

The honeysuckle is known for its delightful nectar. It is also considered a symbol of devotion. Honeysuckle is one of the most highly regarded Chinese herbs for promoting detoxification and cleansing of the body. It is used to treat fever and inflammation, to reduce blood pressure, and as an expectorant for coughs. It is also said to reduce freckles. Chamomile is a relaxing digestive that soothes and relaxes the whole body. This is just the tea to have after a stressful day.

Makes 1 cup (8 fl oz/250 ml)
serves 1

2 teaspoons dried honeysuckle flowers
1 teaspoon dried chamomile flowers
1 cup (8 fl oz/250 ml) boiling water

Combine the honeysuckle and chamomile in a warmed small ceramic or glass teapot. Add the boiling water, cover, and let steep for 10 minutes. Strain, then drink hot.

Note: To help reduce freckles, make a strong infusion of 1 cup (8 fl oz/250 ml) of crushed honeysuckle flowers (use fresh flowers if available) to 2 cups (16 fl oz/500 ml) of boiling water. Infuse for 15 minutes. Bathe face regularly in the infusion and/or add infusion to bath water.

Elder Flower, Yarrow, and Clove Tea

The elder tree produces batch after batch of creamy white flowers that have a mucilaginous property when taken internally, coating and soothing the throat. The strong decongestant effect of these flowers makes elder valuable for treating colds and chills. But beware if planting; once an elder takes root, little elders will pop up everywhere. Yarrow is a small plant that bears white or purple umbrella-shaped flowers with a distinct odor and flavor. Yarrow is traditionally used as a steptic (to stop bleeding), due to its ability to strengthen blood vessels. Both these plants grow easily in backyards and are great for relieving flu symptoms. Cloves add flavor and increase the warming actions of the elder and yarrow.

Makes 2 cups (16 fl oz/500 ml)
serves 2–3

2–3 tablespoons chopped fresh elder flowers
1–2 tablespoons chopped fresh yarrow flowers
1/2 teaspoon ground cloves
2 cups (16 fl oz/500 ml) boiling water

Combine the elder flowers, yarrow flowers and cloves in a warmed ceramic or glass teapot. Add the boiling water, cover, and let steep for 10–15 minutes. Strain, then drink hot.

Drink 1 cup 3 times a day for colds and influenza.

Mallow and Peppermint Tea

Mallow was known as a cure-all in the 16th century. It has the ability to increase mothers' breast milk, to relieve sore, swollen breasts, and to soothe urinary tract infections. Mallow has a slightly astringent taste and can be applied externally to soothe weeping eczema, boils, and abscesses. Mallow flowers and leaves are used for coughs, sore throats, and emphysema. Peppermint, with its aromatic menthols, lends a stimulating flavor to this floral tea. It absorbs wind and is an excellent carminative; it also stops nausea and vomiting.

Makes 1 cup (8 fl oz/250 ml)
serves 1

1 teaspoon dried mallow flowers and/or leaves
1/2 teaspoon crumbled dried peppermint leaves
1 cup (8 fl oz/250 ml) boiling water

Combine the mallow and peppermint in a warmed small ceramic or glass teapot. Add the boiling water, cover, and let steep for 10 minutes. Strain, then drink hot.

Mullein and Angelica Tea

The yellow flowers of the mullein plant have been used to treat tuberculosis and other chest conditions, such as bronchitis, asthma, and whooping cough. An oil made from the flowers is used to treat hemorrhoids and ear infections. Mullein is best for treating dry, hard coughs. Angelica has been used for years as a sweet. It has warming medicinal properties and produces green-white flowers with a pleasant scent. The pretty flowers combine with mullein to make a relaxing expectorant and carminative. Honey may be added to taste, if desired.

Makes 1 cup (8 fl oz/250 ml)
serves 1

2 teaspoons mullein flowers, leaves and/or seeds
1 teaspoon angelica flowers, leaves, root, and/or seeds
1 cup (8 fl oz/250 ml) boiling water

Combine the mullein and angelica in a warmed small ceramic or glass teapot or cup. Add the boiling water, cover, and let steep for 20 minutes. Strain, then drink hot.

Drink up to 3 cups of this tea each day during an illness.

Lavender and Marshmallow Tea

Lavender has many therapeutic properties that help to relax the body during stressful situations. Aromatic lavender tea can help with problems such as headaches, low spirits, muscle tension, and nervous debility. Taking an infusion of lavender after a hard day at home or work can carry your worries away. It can also induce a peaceful, blissful slumber for those who have trouble falling asleep. As an infusion, it combines well with rosemary, skullcap, or chamomile. Lavender's purple-flowering blossoms have long been picked, dried, and placed in cupboards as sachets, or used to deter insects. Marshmallow has delicate pink flowers and is hard to find commercially, but it can be grown at home. It has a cool, moist, sweet character and is an effective, yet gentle cough expectorant.

Makes 2 cups (16 fl oz/250 ml)
serves 2–3

2 teaspoons lavender flowers and/or leaves
2 teaspoons marshmallow flowers, leaves and/or root
2 cups (16 fl oz/500 ml) boiling water

Combine the lavender and marshmallow in a warmed ceramic or glass teapot. Add the boiling water, cover, and let steep for 10 minutes. Strain, then drink hot.

Drink up to 3 cups a day if needed.

Right: Lavender and Marshmallow Tea

Rose Petal, Hibiscus, and Orange Zest Tea

The rose has a long history of medicinal use; its Latin name, *Rosa canina*, was given to it because of its history of being used to treat dog bites. An old herbal publication, *Askham's Herbal* (1550AD), says "Drye roses put to ye nose to smell do comforte the braine and the heart and quenche sprite." Chinese herbalists use rose petals as a blood tonic and to stimulate the liver. Hibiscus and the orange zest add a tangy flavor and vitamin C to this tea, making it a good winter beverage for colds and flus.

Makes 1 cup (8 fl oz/250 ml)
serves 1

2 teaspoons fresh rose petals
1 teaspoon dried hibiscus calyces
1/2 teaspoon grated orange zest (rind)
1 cup (8 fl oz/250 ml) boiling water

Combine the rose petals, hibiscus and orange zest in a warmed small ceramic or glass teapot or cup. Add the boiling water, cover, and let steep for 10 minutes. Strain, then drink hot.

Drink 1 to 2 cups of the tea each day.

Yarrow and Cinnamon Tea

Yarrow is one of the best blood-vessel tonics there is. It improves venous return and fluid retention, and it is also valued as a treatment for colds and flu. Yarrow dilates blood vessels, thus decreasing blood pressure and improving blood flow throughout the body, especially for intermittent claudication. The flowers are antiallergic and expel heat from the body by causing sweating. Their bitter taste can be masked with the pleasant flavor of cinnamon, which also acts as an aromatic astringent, heating the body in cold temperatures. Cinnamon has been used for thousands of years to ease nausea and vomiting.

Makes 1 cup (8 fl oz/250 ml)
serves 1

2 teaspoons chopped fresh yarrow flowers
1/4 teaspoon ground cinnamon
1 cup (8 fl oz/250 ml) boiling water

Combine the yarrow and cinnamon in a warmed small ceramic or glass teapot or cup. Add the boiling water, cover, and let steep for 5–10 minutes. Strain, then drink hot.

Drink up to 3 cups a day.

Right: Yarrow and Cinnamon Tea

Tea from Your Garden

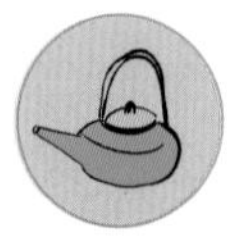

Many of the plants used to make tea are easy to grow. Most are hardy and grow well. When purchasing plants, make sure you buy the correct species by checking the Latin names. A good pictorial book will help to identify them. Some plants to grow at home include:

Trees

Elder (*Sambucus nigra*)
Ginkgo (*Ginkgo biloba*)
Hibiscus (*Hibiscus rosa-sinensis*)
Mulberry (*Morus nigra*)
Rose (*Rosa* spp.)
Tea (*Camellia sinensis*)

Small Plants, Shrubs and Bushes

Calendula (*Calendula officinalis*)
Chamomile (German) (*Matracaria recutita*)
Dandelion (*Taraxacum officinalis*)
Echinacea (*Echinacea* spp.)
Fennel (*Foeniculum vulgare*)
Feverfew (*Tanacetum parthenium*)
Globe artichoke (*Cynara scolymus*)
Ginger (*Zingiber officinale*)
Hawthorn (*Crataegus oxycanthoides*)
Juniper (*Juniper communis*)
Lavender (*Lavendula angustifolia*)
Lemon verbena (*Lippia citriodora*)
Nasturtium (*Tropaeolum majus*)
Passionflower (*Passiflora incarnata*)
Peppermint (*Mentha x piperita*)
Ribwort (*Plantago major*)
Rosemary (*Rosemarinus officinalis*)
Sage (*Salvia officinalis*)
Strawberry (*Fragaria vesca*)
St. John's Wort (*Hypericum perforatum*)
Sunflower (*Helianthus annus*)
Thyme (*thymus vulgaris*)
Valerian (*Valeriana officinalis*)
Yarrow (*Achillea millefolium*)

Harvesting

Harvest the uppermost parts of a plant on a dry day, just after the morning dew has dried and before the heat of the sun, usually between 9 and 10 am.

When picking leaves, choose the top leaves on the outside of the bush or plant. They should be fully mature and bright green. Cut stems with sharp scissors or clippers. Strip off strong leaves by running your hand down the stem firmly but gently. For softer leaves, pick one at a time to prevent damage. Flowers are best picked just before or immediately after they begin to bloom.

Roots should be harvested in autumn or winter when the plant has gone dormant for winter. Dig a wide circle around the plant. then gently remove some of the roots. Don't harvest more than half the root or that will kill the tree or shrub. The exception is dandelion, which tends to multiply voraciously and can be pulled out whole.

Drying

Plants should be dried immediately after picking. Spread the leaves, flowers, or roots on a gauze or mesh tray so there is plenty of air circulation. Be sure to spread them evenly, as drying them too close together will cause mold. Longer-stemmed plants can be cut and tied in bunches, covered with a paper bag, then hung upside down to dry in a dark, open cupboard or well-ventilated shed.

The ideal temperature for drying is 90°F (25–35°C). Cover mesh trays with paper at night to prevent insect infestation. Leaves and flowers can also be dried in an oven at 100°F (38°C).

After drying, plants should retain much of their original color and be dry enough to crackle. This indicates that they have been dried correctly, with minimal loss of essential oils and medicinal value.

Storing

Put the herbs in dark, dry, airtight glass containers, and store away from heat and light. Label every container with the plant name and date stored. Dried herbs will keep for 1–2 years. Store them whole and crumble just before making tea or when using in cooking.

Creating Your Own Special Blends

Creating and experimenting with different tastes can be exciting. Some people like slightly bitter herbs. These can be teamed with nutmeg or cinnamon in an infused tea or simply brewed with lemongrass. Green teas tend to be slightly bitter, and the longer you brew the leaves in the hot water the more bitter they will become.

For sweet herbal teas, look for dried berries. These look attractive in glass teapots, as do flowers. The herb that is a must in the kitchen is licorice root. It blends well with all other herbs, yet it usually masks the flavor of other ingredients.

When brewing green teas, such as the fragrant Matcha, Sencha, or Gyokuro, never use a strainer. The leaf needs to be relaxed, or loose, so it can unfold, open up and release its flavor. The beauty behind this process is that each and every infusion will taste different. While some teas become lighter and milder with each brew, others become richer and fuller. If serving several people, pour a little tea into each cup, then come back and top them all up again. In China, tea is served from left to right, then from left to right again. This way everyone will get a similar-tasting tea. Return strained tea leaves to the teapot, and remember—do not leave any leaves soaking in hot water, strain it all off.

A very important point to remember is to never use a herb that you have not identified properly. Buy a good pictorial medicinal herb book that will help you identify various herbs or ask at your local plant nursery.

Keep all your herbs in jars, clearly labeled with the date, Latin and common names, along with what they are used for. Labeling will help remind you what works best for specific health problems. Once you have a selection of tea ingredients, you can display them in your kitchen so that you can offer choices to your guests. I have found over the years that guests are always keen to try one of my new brews. They tend to have their own special requests for a certain tea or herbal infusion. It definitely makes a pleasant change from the usual question, "Would you like tea or coffee?"

tea chart

Herb or Tea	Function	Health Benefit
Alfalfa (lucerne)	A relaxing nutritive, tonifying to the blood vessels	A tonic after blood loss and used to help reduce bleeding
Aniseed	An antiseptic and a cough expectorant; soothes abdominal cramps and spasms	Soothes coughs, chest infections, and colic with flatulence
Bilberry	Reduces blood sugar levels; an astringent and strong antioxidant for the eyes	Helps glaucoma, diabetes, and tired, bloodshot eyes
Black tea	A stimulant and a digestive; also an eye wash	Assists when you are feeling tired and out of sorts; gives you some get up and go
Buchu	A diuretic antiseptic to the urinary tract, with antibacterial activity	Use when there is blood and mucus in urine, indicating an infection in the urinary tract
Calendula	A strong anti-inflammatory, antiseptic, and antifungal; also a lymphatic cleanser	Helps whenever lymph glands are affected, as with glandular fever
Chamomile (German)	A bitter sedative, relaxing to the whole body; anti-inflammatory	Assists with insomnia and/or flatulence, cramping, and discomfort
Corn silk	Soothing to the urinary tract and respiratory system, diuretic and tonifying to the urinary tract	Helps with cystitis and bedwetting; prevents stone buildup in the kidneys
Dandelion	A diuretic rich in potassium, and also a digestive tonic, cleansing to rheumatic joints	Use for edema and indigestion, chronic skin conditions and arthritis
Elder	A diuretic, diaphoretic, and a gentle expectorant	For use when you have colds, flu, and sinus trouble, and for any catarrhal inflammation of the upper respiratory system
Eyebright	An anticatarrhal and anti-inflammatory, with an astringent effect	Specifically used for mucous membrane conditions, sinusitis, congestion, and phlegmy throat
Fennel	An antiseptic, antispasmodic expectorant that has relaxing actions on the digestive system	Relieves wind and cramping, and has a relaxing action on coughing; the oils are antiseptic for chest colds

Herb or Tea	Function	Health Benefit
Ginger	Warming to the body; an antinausea carminative and anti-inflammatory; diaphoretic (promotes a sweat)	For arthritis and tummy upsets, motion sickness, and fever
Ginseng	Increases and improves mental and physical performance	For the elderly and debilitated, to counteract memory loss, and to fortify after illness
Green tea	A digestive and a mild stimulant; nourishing and protective against cancer	Drink with meals to aid digestion; also acts as an antioxidant
Hawthorn	Decreases blood pressure and tonifies heart tissue; dilates peripheral blood vessels	Helps with hypertension, palpitations, and intermittent claudication
Hibiscus	An astringent with a citrus flavor; added to different tea blends	A tangy addition to other teas; a tonic for colds due to vitamin C content
Licorice	Known by herbalists as a panacea or cure-all, an anticatarrhal, an antiallergic anti–inflammatory, and an expectorant that soothes and heals digestive ulcers	Relieves coughs, colds, sore throats and flu. Assists in fever management, aids decongestion and soothes ulcers of the digestive tract
Oat Straw	Relaxing and nourishing to the nervous system, rich in calcium and fiber, helps alleviate rheumatic or back pain	Benefits a neurotic nervous personality, and alleviates debility and fatigue due to chronic nervousness; used in the bath for aches and pain
Rosemary	A warming digestive remedy and a relaxing antiseptic that promotes sweating; an antidepressant and brain stimulant	Aids indigestion, memory loss, low spirits, hair loss, and arthritis and related congestion
St John's wort	A sedative and tonic for the nervous system	For hysteria, low spirits, apathy, and fatigue from ill feelings
Thyme	A strong cleansing chest antiseptic; antimicrobial and carminative	Relieves bronchitis, asthma, gum and mouth infections, and bed-wetting
Yarrow	A peripheral vasodilator, tonic to all the blood vessels; an antispasmodic	Balances menstrual problems and manages fever and heavy bleeding; use topically as a poultice to heal wounds

glossary

Adaptogen: A herb that can help the body respond more favorably to stress by nurturing and strengthening that particular part of the body.

Adrenal glands: Glands situated at the top of each kidney that secrete the hormones adrenaline and nor adrenaline: the hormones responsible for the "fight or flight" response to sudden stress.

Antihistamine: A substance that stops histamine reaction by binding to histamine receptor sites in body tissue.

Anti-inflammatory: A substance that decreases or stops inflammation.

Antioxidant: A substance that inhibits destructive oxidation in the body; some examples are vitamins C and E, selenium and green tea.

Astringent: A substance that has a drying effect, tightening and toning the cells and mucous membranes.

Bioflavonoids: Plant pigments (usually yellow in color) also known as vitamin P. They include rutin, quercetin, and hesperidin, and they have potent anti-inflammatory actions and improve the absorption of vitamin C.

Bud: The unopened leaf at the very top of a tree/bush, sought after for its tenderness and sweetness.

Carminative: An herb that decreases flatulence and relaxes the muscles in the body by decreasing tension.

Cha: Japanese for "tea".

Chanoyu: Japanese for "hot water for tea".

Cystitis: An infection or inflammation of the urinary bladder.

Decongestant: An herb or remedy that removes mucus congestion from the body.

Dehydration: When the body is lacking in water.

Diuretic: A herb or remedy that increases urinary output.

Dyspnea: Shortness of breath and difficulty in breathing.

Dust: Powdery pieces of tea, less than 0.04 inch (1 mm) in length.

Edema: Fluid retention that results in swelling, usually of the limbs.

Emphysema: A disease of the alveoli in the lungs, where the alveoli are permanently expanded and inflamed by an overproduction of mucus, which causes difficulty in breathing.

Expectorant: An herb or remedy that increases the removal of mucus from the lungs.

Fermentation: When the tea leaves become oxidized, the cell structure is changed, and the leaf becomes darker, drier and richer in flavor.

Formosa: (Former name of Taiwan) an island off the coast of China that grows Oolong, Pouchong and black teas.

Glaucoma: A disease of the eye where there is increased pressure in the eye fluids, which results in a progressive loss of eyesight.

Gout: A painful inflammation, usually of the big toe or other joints, caused by uric acid buildup in the joints.

Insomnia: The inability to sleep.

Intermittent claudication: An initial symptom of arteriosclerosis, which manifests as pain, cramps or a tired feeling in the limbs, especially in the calf muscle.

Jaundice: An increase of bile in the blood, resulting in a yellowing of the skin and sclera (white sections) of the eyes, loss of appetite, and lethargy.

Magnesium: An important mineral in the body, responsible for muscle relaxation and contraction. It works closely with calcium.

Menopause: When a woman ceases to menstruate.

Mucilaginous: Refers to the nature of mucilage, i.e., various gummy secretions present in plants.

Mucus: A viscid fluid secreted by the inner lining of the digestive tract, glands, and lungs. During a disease state, it may be oversecreted and be present as phlegm in the respiratory system.

Mucous membranes: Membranes that line the whole digestive tract from mouth to anus, and other organs. They secrete mucus to coat and protect.

Palpitation: An abnormal throbbing of the heart that can be felt by the person.

Pan-fired: Green tea that has been steamed then rolled in woks or pans over charcoal. This process ensures even drying of the leaves, enhancing their quality and flavor.

Phytoestrogens: Plant compounds that have an estrogenic effect within the body.

Polyphenols: Chemical compounds found in certain substances, that have disinfective and antiseptic qualities.

Rolling: An action that releases essential oils in tea leaves.

Reflux: The back flow of food up the esophagus, usually caused by indigestion.

Steptic: A remedy that can stop bleeding.

Stomachic: A remedy that is nourishing and soothing to the digestive system.

Tannin: An astringent chemical found in some herbs and in the tea plant.

Tatami: A Japanese straw mat; laid on the floor during the tea ceremony.

Tip: The bud leaf on a tea plant.

Tonifying: The healing and improving of the function of organs or tissues.

Withering: The first stage in making black tea. It reduces moisture so that the leaf can be macerated (softened) or rolled.

Botanical Names

alfalfa (*Medicago sativa*)
angelica (*Angelica archangelica*)
aniseed (*Pimpinella anisum*)
astragalus (*Astragalus membranaceus*)
bilberry (*Vaccinium myrtilis*)
black cohosh (*Cimicifuga racemosa*)
black currant (*Ribes nigrum*)
buchu (*Barosima betulina*)
calendula (*Calendula officinalis*)
cardamom (*Elattaria cardamomum*)
chamomile (*Matracaria recutita*)
chickweed (*Stellaria media*)
chrysanthemum (*Chrysanthemum* x *morifolium*)
cinnamon (*Cinnamomum verum*)
clivers (*Galium aparine*)
clove (*Syzygium aromaticum*)
corn silk (*Zea mays*)
dandelion (*Taraxacum radix*)
echinacea (*Echinacea purpurea/angustifolia*)
elder (*Sambucus nigra*)
elderberry (*Sambucus nigra*)
elecampane (*Inula helenium*)
eyebright (*Euphrasia officinalis*)
fennel (*Foeniculum vulgare*)
ginger (*Zingiber officinale*)
golden rod (*Solidago virgaurea*)
gotu kola (*Centella asciatica*)
hawthorn (*Crataegus* spp.)
hibiscus (*Hibiscus rosa-sinensis*)
honeysuckle (*Lonicera japonica*)
hop (*Humulus lupulus*)
horehound (*Marribum vulgare*)
juniper (*Juniperus communis*)
Korean ginseng (*Panax ginseng*)
lavender (*Lavendula angustifolia*)
lemon (*Citrus limon*)
lemon balm (*Melissa officinalis*)
lemon grass (*Cymbogon citratus*)
licorice (*Glyccyrrhiza glabra*)
lime (*Tilia europea*)
mallow (*Malva sylvestris*)
marshmallow (*Althaea officinalis*)
meadow sweet (*Filipendula ulmaria*)
mullein (*Verbascum thapsus*)
nettle (*Urtica diocia*)
oak bark (*Quercus robur*)
oat straw (*Avena sativa*)
orange (*Citrus sinensis*)
passionflower (*Passiflora incarnata*)
peach (*Prunus persica*)
peppermint (*Mentha* x *piperita*)
plantain, see ribwort
raspberry (*Rubus idaeus*)
red clover (*Trifolium pratense*)
ribwort (*Plantago major*)
rose (*Rosa* spp.)
rosemary (*Rosmarinus officinalis*)
sage (*Salvia officinalis*)
Seville orange (*Citrus aurantium/Citrus reticulata*)
Siberian ginseng (*Eleutherococcus senticosus*)
skullcap (*Scutellaria lateriflora*)
St. John's wort (*Hypericum perforatum*)
strawberry (*Fragaria vesca*)
tea (*Camellia sinensis*)
thyme (*Thymus vulgarus*)
uva ursi (*Arctostophylos uva-ursi*)
valerian (*Valeriana officinalis*)
vervain (*Verbena officinalis*)
vitex (*Vitex agnus-castus*)
yarrow (*Achillea millefolium*)

ailments index

ingredients index

Recommended Reading

Burgess, Anthony, *The Book of Tea*, New York: Abbeville Press, 1992.

Gary and Zong Xiao-fan, *Chinese Medicinal Teas,* Boulder Colorado: Blue Poppy Press, 1996.

Lu, C. Henry, *Chinese Herbal Cures,* New York: Sterling Publishing, 1991.

Ody, Penelope, *The Complete Medicinal Herbal,* New York: DK Publishing 1993.

Perry, Sara, *The Book of Herbal Teas,* San Francisco: Chronicle Books, 1997.

Rosen, Diana, *Green Tea,* London: Souvenir Press, 2000.

Sach, Penelope, *On Tea and Healthy Living,* Sydney: Allen & Unwin, 1995.

I would like to dedicate this book to my mother and father, who supported me through five years of study to become a herbalist and nutritionist. Also, love and appreciation goes to my daughter, Tania, who patiently waited outside many shops and libraries as I researched this book. I'd also like to extend my heartfelt thanks to my husband, who stepped in and bought me a new computer when mine just would not go any further.

With all my love,

TAMMY

Acknowledgments

Thanks are also due to Danny Lai, traditional Chinese doctor, Bankstown NSW; The Tea Centre of Sydney, NSW; Chinese Ginsengs and Herbs, Haymarket NSW; Tea Temple, Sydney NSW; Live Craft Centre, Sydney, NSW.

Herb and Tea Websites

www.oracletree.com; www.jairamdass.com; www.australherbs.com.au; www.tassie.net.au/tasherbs/; www.organicherbfarm.com; www.ermasherbs.com; www.greentea.com; www.richters.com; www.shraddhaherbal.com; www.shamauniserve.com; www.teatemple.com.au; www.goldleaftea.freeserve.co.uk; www.imperialtea.com; www.mycupoftea.com; www.stashtea.com/; www.teadynasty.com; www.japantea.com; www.orientaid.com/green.htm

Commissioned by Deborah Nixon
Production Manager: Sally Stokes
Text: Tammy Safi
Editorial Consultant: Jan Purser
Photography: Vicki Liley and Simon Kenny
Stylist: Vicki Liley
Designer: Robyn Latimer
Cover Design: David Eldridge, Two Associates
Copy Editors: Joanne Holliman, Carolyn Miller, Sarah Shrubb
Project Coordinator: Kate Merrifield

First published by Lansdowne Publishing Pty Ltd
Sydney NSW 2000, Australia

This edition published by Simon & Schuster UK Ltd, 2011
A CBS COMPANY

1 2 3 4 5 6 7 8 9 10

SIMON AND SCHUSTER ILLUSTRATED BOOKS
Simon & Schuster UK
222 Gray's Inn Road
London WC1X 8HB

www.simonandschuster.co.uk

A CIP catalogue record for this book is available from the British Library

ISBN 978-0-85720-262-8

Set in Giovanni and Democratica on QuarkXPress
Printed in Singapore by Tien Wah Press (Pte) Ltd